Dear Traveler,

Thank you for purchasing The Ultimate Travel Tracker.

As as traveler who has explored over 50 countries across seven continents, I know the importance of logging every precious passport stamp. In my quest to find the perfect system for tracking my solo, couple, and family adventures, I have purchased many travel journals. But I wasn't happy with any of them.

So I decided to fix that.

The Ultimate Travel Tracker was created by travelers for travelers. It is the best way to document your adventures in a single, comprehensive journal.

If you agree that The Ultimate Travel Tracker is awesome, please leave a review.

And if you're looking for some travel inspiration, please check out *THE PASSPORT PROJECT*. (Warning: If you read it, you WILL be infected with the travel bug.)

Dream big and travel far,

Kellie McIntyre

Author of *THE PASSPORT PROJECT*
4WornPassports.com

The Ultimate Travel Tracker: 195 Countries of the World + Special Territories

For bulk sales, permission requests, and corrections, please visit:
ShamrockHousePublishing.com

ISBN: 978-1-7377438-5-9

Published by Shamrock House, Birmingham, Alabama
1 3 5 7 9 10 8 6 4 2

SHAMROCK
HOUSE

This journal belongs to:

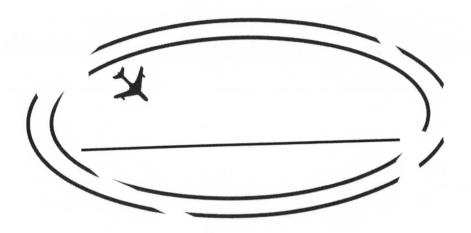

If found, please contact:

_____

_____

_____

My Travel Tracker

[] AFRICA (54)

[] Algeria
[] Angola
[] Benin
[] Botswana
[] Burkina Faso
[] Burundi
[] Cameroon
[] Cape Verde
[] Cent. Afr. Rep.
[] Chad
[] Comoros
[] Congo
[] Dem. Rep. Congo
[] Djibouti
[] Egypt
[] Equatorial Guinea
[] Eritrea
[] Eswatini (Swaziland)
[] Ethiopia
[] Gabon
[] Gambia
[] Ghana
[] Guinea
[] Guinea-Bissau
[] Ivory Coast
[] Kenya
[] Lesotho
[] Liberia
[] Libya
[] Madagascar
[] Malawi
[] Mali
[] Mauritania
[] Mauritius

[] Morocco
[] Mozambique
[] Namibia
[] Niger
[] Nigeria
[] Rwanda
[] Sao Tome & Principe
[] Senegal
[] Seychelles
[] Sierra Leone
[] Somalia
[] South Africa
[] South Sudan
[] Sudan
[] Tanzania
[] Togo
[] Tunisia
[] Uganda
[] Zambia
[] Zimbabwe

[] ANTARCTICA

[] ASIA (48)

[] Afghanistan
[] Armenia
[] Azerbaijan
[] Bahrain
[] Bangladesh
[] Bhutan
[] Brunei
[] Cambodia
[] China
[] Cyprus
[] Georgia
[] India
[] Indonesia

[] Iran
[] Iraq
[] Israel
[] Japan
[] Jordan
[] Kazakhstan
[] Kuwait
[] Kyrgyzstan
[] Laos
[] Lebanon
[] Malaysia
[] Maldives
[] Mongolia
[] Myanmar/Burma
[] Nepal
[] North Korea
[] Oman
[] Pakistan
[] Palestine*
[] Philippines
[] Qatar
[] Saudi Arabia
[] Singapore
[] South Korea
[] Sri Lanka
[] Syria
[] Tajikistan
[] Thailand
[] Timor-Leste
[] Turkey
[] Turkmenistan
[] UAE
[] Uzbekistan
[] Vietnam
[] Yemen

195 Countries of the World

[] AUSTRALIA/ OCEANIA (14)

[] Australia
[] Fiji
[] Kiribati
[] Marshall Islands
[] Micronesia
[] Nauru
[] New Zealand
[] Palau
[] Papua New Guinea
[] Samoa
[] Solomon Islands
[] Tonga
[] Tuvalu
[] Vanuatu

[] EUROPE (44)

[] Albania
[] Andorra
[] Austria
[] Belarus
[] Belgium
[] Bosnia and
   Herzegovina
[] Bulgaria
[] Croatia
[] Czech Republic
[] Denmark
[] Estonia
[] Finland
[] France
[] Germany
[] Greece
[] Holy See (Vatican)*

[] Hungary
[] Iceland
[] Ireland
[] Italy
[] Latvia
[] Liechtenstein
[] Lithuania
[] Luxembourg
[] Malta
[] Moldova
[] Monaco
[] Montenegro
[] Netherlands
[] North Macedonia
[] Norway
[] Poland
[] Portugal
[] Romania
[] Russia
[] San Marino
[] Serbia
[] Slovakia
[] Slovenia
[] Spain
[] Sweden
[] Switzerland
[] Ukraine
[] United Kingdom

[] NORTH AMERICA (23)

[] Antigua & Barbuda
[] The Bahamas
[] Barbados
[] Belize

[] Canada
[] Costa Rica
[] Cuba
[] Dominica
[] Dominican Rep
[] El Salvador
[] Grenada
[] Guatemala
[] Haiti
[] Honduras
[] Jamaica
[] Mexico
[] Nicaragua
[] Panama
[] St Kitts & Nevis
[] Saint Lucia
[] Saint Vincent &
   the Grenadines
[] Trinidad & Tobago
[] USA

[] SOUTH AMERICA (12)

[] Argentina
[] Bolivia
[] Brazil
[] Chile
[] Colombia
[] Ecuador
[] Guyana
[] Paraguay
[] Peru
[] Suriname
[] Uruguay
[] Venezuela

*The previous list includes the 193 countries of the United Nations (UN) plus Holy See (Vatican City) and the State of Palestine, which are UN non-member observer states. Official countries and territories change occasionally due to political circumstances.

39 Special Territories

Africa (4)

[] Mayotte (FR)
[] Réunion (FR)
[] Saint Helena (UK)
[] Western Sahara

Asia (3)

[] Hong Kong (CN)
[] Macau (CN)
[] Taiwan (CN)

Europe (3)

[] Faroe Islands (DK)
[] Gibraltar (UK)
[] Isle of Man (UK)

North America/ Caribbean (18)

[] Anguilla (UK)
[] Aruba (NL)
[] Bermuda (UK)
[] British Virgin Islands
[] Caribbean Netherlands
[] Cayman Islands (UK)
[] Curaçao (NL)
[] Greenland (DK)
[] Guadaloupe (FR)
[] Martinique (FR)
[] Montserrat (UK)
[] St. Bart (FR)
[] St. Martin (FR)
[] Sint Maarten (NL)
[] Puerto Rico (US)
[] Turks and Caicos (UK)
[] US Virgin Islands
[] St. Pierre & Miquel. (FR)

Oceania (9)

[] American Samoa (US)
[] Cook Islands (NZ)
[] French Polynesia (FR)
[] Guam (US)
[] New Caledonia (FR)
[] Niue (NZ)
[] No Mariana Islands (US)
[] Tokelau (NZ)
[] Wallis & Futuna (FR)

South America (2)

[] Falkland Islands (UK)
[] French Guiana (FR)

Africa

There is nothing like returning to a place
that remains unchanged to find the ways in
which you yourself have altered.

—Nelson Mandela

Algeria

Draw the flag

ARRIVED   DEPARTED

Travel buddies:

Arrived by:

Highs F/C____ Lows F/C____

Currency:

Exchange: ____ = ____

HOW DO YOU SAY?

Language:
_____

Hello: Goodbye:

Please: Thank you:

Sights
☆☆☆☆☆
☆☆☆☆☆
☆☆☆☆☆
☆☆☆☆☆
☆☆☆☆☆

Cities
☆☆☆☆☆
☆☆☆☆☆
☆☆☆☆☆
☆☆☆☆☆
☆☆☆☆☆

I'll never forget:

_____
_____
_____
_____
_____
_____

OVERALL RATING: ☆☆☆☆☆

Angola

Draw the flag

ARRIVED | DEPARTED

Travel buddies:

Arrived by:

Highs F/C____ Lows F/C____

Currency:
Exchange: _____ = _____

HOW DO YOU SAY?

Language:
_____

Hello: Goodbye:

Please: Thank you:

Sights
☆☆☆☆☆
☆☆☆☆☆
☆☆☆☆☆
☆☆☆☆☆
☆☆☆☆☆

Cities
☆☆☆☆☆
☆☆☆☆☆
☆☆☆☆☆
☆☆☆☆☆
☆☆☆☆☆

I'll never forget:
_____
_____
_____
_____
_____

OVERALL RATING: ☆☆☆☆☆

Benin

Draw the flag

ARRIVED | DEPARTED

Travel buddies:

Arrived by:

Highs F/C____ Lows F/C____

Currency:

Exchange: ____ = ____

HOW DO YOU SAY?

Language:

_____

Hello:

Please:

Goodbye:

Thank you:

Sights		Cities	
☆☆☆☆☆		☆☆☆☆☆	
☆☆☆☆☆		☆☆☆☆☆	
☆☆☆☆☆		☆☆☆☆☆	
☆☆☆☆☆		☆☆☆☆☆	
☆☆☆☆☆		☆☆☆☆☆	

I'll never forget:

_____

_____

_____

_____

_____

OVERALL RATING: ☆☆☆☆☆

Botswana

Draw the flag

ARRIVED   DEPARTED

Travel buddies:

Arrived by:

Highs F/C____ Lows F/C____

Currency:

Exchange: _____ = _____

HOW DO YOU SAY?

Language:
_____

Hello:

Goodbye:

Please:

Thank you:

Sights

☆☆☆☆☆
☆☆☆☆☆
☆☆☆☆☆
☆☆☆☆☆
☆☆☆☆☆

Cities

☆☆☆☆☆
☆☆☆☆☆
☆☆☆☆☆
☆☆☆☆☆
☆☆☆☆☆

I'll never forget:

_____

_____

_____

_____

_____

OVERALL RATING: ☆☆☆☆☆

Burkina Faso

Draw the flag

ARRIVED   DEPARTED

Highs F/C____ Lows F/C____

Travel buddies:

Arrived by:

Currency:

Exchange: _____ = _____

HOW DO YOU SAY?

Language:

_____

Hello:

Please:

Goodbye:

Thank you:

Sights
☆☆☆☆☆
☆☆☆☆☆
☆☆☆☆☆
☆☆☆☆☆
☆☆☆☆☆

Cities
☆☆☆☆☆
☆☆☆☆☆
☆☆☆☆☆
☆☆☆☆☆
☆☆☆☆☆

I'll never forget:

_____

_____

_____

_____

_____

OVERALL RATING: ☆☆☆☆☆

Burundi

Draw the flag

ARRIVED   DEPARTED

Highs F/C____ Lows F/C____

Travel buddies:

Arrived by:

Currency:

Exchange: _____ = _____

HOW DO YOU SAY?

Language:
_____

Hello:

Goodbye:

Please:

Thank you:

Sights

☆☆☆☆☆
☆☆☆☆☆
☆☆☆☆☆
☆☆☆☆☆
☆☆☆☆☆

Cities

☆☆☆☆☆
☆☆☆☆☆
☆☆☆☆☆
☆☆☆☆☆
☆☆☆☆☆

I'll never forget:

OVERALL RATING: ☆☆☆☆☆

Cameroon

Draw the flag

ARRIVED | DEPARTED

Travel buddies:

Arrived by:

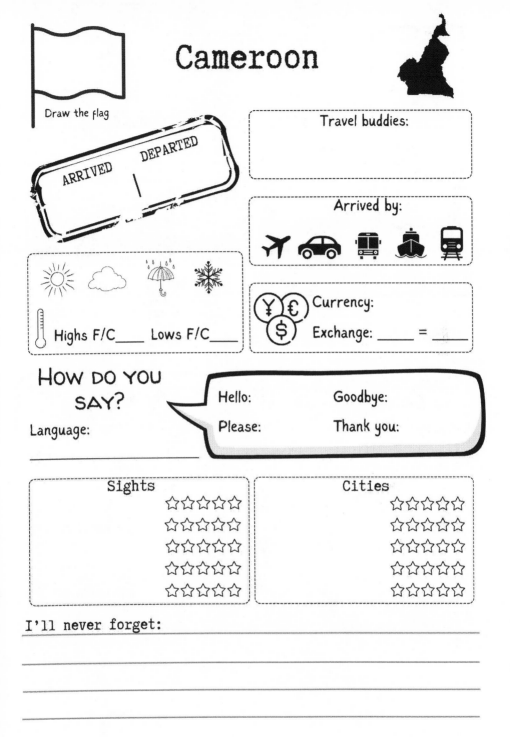

Currency:

Exchange: _____ = _____

Highs F/C____ Lows F/C____

HOW DO YOU SAY?

Language:

_____

Hello:

Goodbye:

Please:

Thank you:

Sights
☆☆☆☆☆
☆☆☆☆☆
☆☆☆☆☆
☆☆☆☆☆
☆☆☆☆☆

Cities
☆☆☆☆☆
☆☆☆☆☆
☆☆☆☆☆
☆☆☆☆☆
☆☆☆☆☆

I'll never forget:

_____

_____

_____

_____

_____

OVERALL RATING: ☆☆☆☆☆

Cape Verde

Draw the flag

ARRIVED   DEPARTED

Highs F/C____   Lows F/C____

Travel buddies:

Arrived by:

Currency:
Exchange: _____ = _____

HOW DO YOU SAY?

Language:
_____

Hello: Goodbye:

Please: Thank you:

Sights
☆☆☆☆☆
☆☆☆☆☆
☆☆☆☆☆
☆☆☆☆☆
☆☆☆☆☆

Cities
☆☆☆☆☆
☆☆☆☆☆
☆☆☆☆☆
☆☆☆☆☆
☆☆☆☆☆

I'll never forget:
_____
_____
_____
_____
_____

OVERALL RATING: ☆☆☆☆☆

Central African Republic

Draw the flag

ARRIVED | DEPARTED

Travel buddies:

Arrived by:

Highs F/C____ Lows F/C____

Currency:

Exchange: _____ = _____

HOW DO YOU SAY?

Language:
_____

Hello:

Goodbye:

Please:

Thank you:

Sights		Cities	
☆☆☆☆☆		☆☆☆☆☆	
☆☆☆☆☆		☆☆☆☆☆	
☆☆☆☆☆		☆☆☆☆☆	
☆☆☆☆☆		☆☆☆☆☆	
☆☆☆☆☆		☆☆☆☆☆	

I'll never forget:

OVERALL RATING: ☆☆☆☆☆

Chad

Draw the flag

ARRIVED   DEPARTED

Travel buddies:

Arrived by:

Highs F/C____ Lows F/C____

Currency:

Exchange: _____ = _____

HOW DO YOU SAY?

Language:
_____

Hello:

Goodbye:

Please:

Thank you:

Sights

☆☆☆☆☆
☆☆☆☆☆
☆☆☆☆☆
☆☆☆☆☆
☆☆☆☆☆

Cities

☆☆☆☆☆
☆☆☆☆☆
☆☆☆☆☆
☆☆☆☆☆
☆☆☆☆☆

I'll never forget:

_____
_____
_____
_____
_____

OVERALL RATING: ☆☆☆☆☆

Comoros

Draw the flag

ARRIVED   DEPARTED

Travel buddies:

Arrived by:

Highs F/C____   Lows F/C____

Currency:

Exchange: _____ = _____

HOW DO YOU SAY?

Language:
_____

Hello: Goodbye:

Please: Thank you:

Sights
☆☆☆☆☆
☆☆☆☆☆
☆☆☆☆☆
☆☆☆☆☆
☆☆☆☆☆

Cities
☆☆☆☆☆
☆☆☆☆☆
☆☆☆☆☆
☆☆☆☆☆
☆☆☆☆☆

I'll never forget:
_____
_____
_____
_____
_____

OVERALL RATING: ☆☆☆☆☆

Republic of the Congo

Draw the flag

ARRIVED   DEPARTED

Travel buddies:

Arrived by:

Highs F/C____ Lows F/C____

Currency:

Exchange: _____ = _____

HOW DO YOU SAY?

Language:
_____

Hello: Goodbye:

Please: Thank you:

Sights
☆☆☆☆☆
☆☆☆☆☆
☆☆☆☆☆
☆☆☆☆☆
☆☆☆☆☆

Cities
☆☆☆☆☆
☆☆☆☆☆
☆☆☆☆☆
☆☆☆☆☆
☆☆☆☆☆

I'll never forget:
_____
_____
_____
_____
_____
_____

OVERALL RATING: ☆☆☆☆☆

Dem. Rep. of the Congo (DRC)

Draw the flag

ARRIVED | DEPARTED

Travel buddies:

Arrived by:

Highs F/C____ Lows F/C____

Currency:

Exchange: _____ = _____

HOW DO YOU SAY?

Language:

_____

Hello:

Please:

Goodbye:

Thank you:

Sights	
☆☆☆☆☆	
☆☆☆☆☆	
☆☆☆☆☆	
☆☆☆☆☆	
☆☆☆☆☆	

Cities	
☆☆☆☆☆	
☆☆☆☆☆	
☆☆☆☆☆	
☆☆☆☆☆	
☆☆☆☆☆	

I'll never forget:

OVERALL RATING: ☆☆☆☆☆

Djibouti

Draw the flag

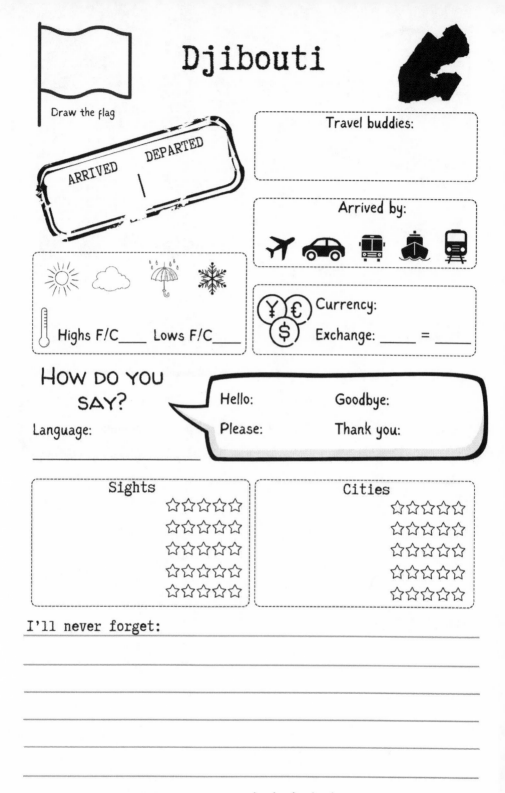

ARRIVED   DEPARTED

Travel buddies:

Arrived by:

Highs F/C____ Lows F/C____

Currency:

Exchange: _____ = _____

HOW DO YOU SAY?

Language:

_____

Hello: Goodbye:

Please: Thank you:

Sights
☆☆☆☆☆
☆☆☆☆☆
☆☆☆☆☆
☆☆☆☆☆
☆☆☆☆☆

Cities
☆☆☆☆☆
☆☆☆☆☆
☆☆☆☆☆
☆☆☆☆☆
☆☆☆☆☆

I'll never forget:

OVERALL RATING: ☆☆☆☆☆

Egypt

Draw the flag

ARRIVED | DEPARTED

Travel buddies:

Arrived by:

Highs F/C____ Lows F/C____

Currency:
Exchange: _____ = _____

HOW DO YOU SAY?

Language:
_____

Hello:

Goodbye:

Please:

Thank you:

Sights

☆☆☆☆☆
☆☆☆☆☆
☆☆☆☆☆
☆☆☆☆☆
☆☆☆☆☆

Cities

☆☆☆☆☆
☆☆☆☆☆
☆☆☆☆☆
☆☆☆☆☆
☆☆☆☆☆

I'll never forget:

_____
_____
_____
_____
_____

OVERALL RATING: ☆☆☆☆☆

Equatorial Guinea

Draw the flag

ARRIVED | DEPARTED

Highs F/C___ Lows F/C___

Travel buddies:

Arrived by:

Currency:
Exchange: _____ = _____

HOW DO YOU SAY?

Language:
_____

Hello:

Goodbye:

Please:

Thank you:

Sights
☆☆☆☆☆
☆☆☆☆☆
☆☆☆☆☆
☆☆☆☆☆
☆☆☆☆☆

Cities
☆☆☆☆☆
☆☆☆☆☆
☆☆☆☆☆
☆☆☆☆☆
☆☆☆☆☆

I'll never forget:
_____
_____
_____
_____
_____
_____

OVERALL RATING: ☆☆☆☆☆

Eritrea

Draw the flag

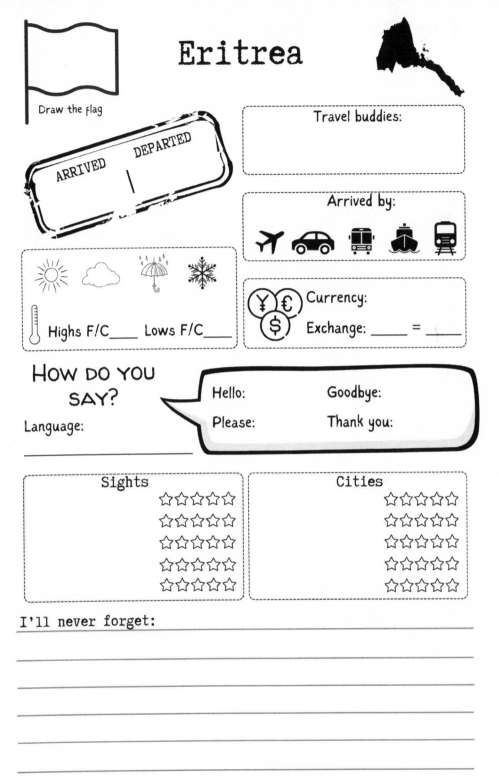

ARRIVED | DEPARTED

Travel buddies:

Arrived by:

Highs F/C____ Lows F/C____

Currency:

Exchange: _____ = _____

HOW DO YOU SAY?

Language:
_____

Hello:

Goodbye:

Please:

Thank you:

Sights
☆☆☆☆☆
☆☆☆☆☆
☆☆☆☆☆
☆☆☆☆☆
☆☆☆☆☆

Cities
☆☆☆☆☆
☆☆☆☆☆
☆☆☆☆☆
☆☆☆☆☆
☆☆☆☆☆

I'll never forget:
_____
_____
_____
_____
_____

OVERALL RATING: ☆☆☆☆☆

Eswatini
(Swaziland)

Draw the flag

ARRIVED · DEPARTED

Highs F/C___ Lows F/C___

Travel buddies:

Arrived by:

Currency:
Exchange: _____ = _____

HOW DO YOU SAY?

Language:
_____

Hello: Goodbye:

Please: Thank you:

Sights
☆☆☆☆☆
☆☆☆☆☆
☆☆☆☆☆
☆☆☆☆☆
☆☆☆☆☆

Cities
☆☆☆☆☆
☆☆☆☆☆
☆☆☆☆☆
☆☆☆☆☆
☆☆☆☆☆

I'll never forget:
_____
_____
_____
_____
_____

OVERALL RATING: ☆☆☆☆☆

Ethiopia

Draw the flag

ARRIVED | DEPARTED

Travel buddies:

Arrived by:

Highs F/C____ Lows F/C____

Currency:

Exchange: _____ = _____

HOW DO YOU SAY?

Language:

_____

Hello:

Goodbye:

Please:

Thank you:

Sights

Cities

I'll never forget:

_____

_____

_____

_____

_____

_____

OVERALL RATING: ☆☆☆☆☆

Gabon

Draw the flag

ARRIVED   DEPARTED

Travel buddies:

Arrived by:

Highs F/C____ Lows F/C____

Currency:

Exchange: _____ = _____

HOW DO YOU SAY?

Language:

_____

Hello: Goodbye:

Please: Thank you:

Sights					
☆☆☆☆☆
☆☆☆☆☆
☆☆☆☆☆
☆☆☆☆☆
☆☆☆☆☆

Cities					
☆☆☆☆☆
☆☆☆☆☆
☆☆☆☆☆
☆☆☆☆☆
☆☆☆☆☆

I'll never forget:

OVERALL RATING: ☆☆☆☆☆

The Gambia

Draw the flag

ARRIVED   DEPARTED

Travel buddies:

Arrived by:

Highs F/C____ Lows F/C____

Currency:

Exchange: ____ = ____

HOW DO YOU SAY?

Language:
_____

Hello: Goodbye:

Please: Thank you:

Sights	Cities
☆☆☆☆☆	☆☆☆☆☆
☆☆☆☆☆	☆☆☆☆☆
☆☆☆☆☆	☆☆☆☆☆
☆☆☆☆☆	☆☆☆☆☆
☆☆☆☆☆	☆☆☆☆☆

I'll never forget:
_____
_____
_____
_____
_____

OVERALL RATING: ☆☆☆☆☆

Ghana

Draw the flag

ARRIVED | DEPARTED

Travel buddies:

Arrived by:

Highs F/C____ Lows F/C____

Currency:
Exchange: ____ = ____

HOW DO YOU SAY?

Language:
_____

Hello: Goodbye:

Please: Thank you:

Sights	Cities
☆☆☆☆☆	☆☆☆☆☆
☆☆☆☆☆	☆☆☆☆☆
☆☆☆☆☆	☆☆☆☆☆
☆☆☆☆☆	☆☆☆☆☆
☆☆☆☆☆	☆☆☆☆☆

I'll never forget:

OVERALL RATING: ☆☆☆☆☆

Guinea

Draw the flag

ARRIVED   DEPARTED

Travel buddies:

Arrived by:

Highs F/C____ Lows F/C____

Currency:

Exchange: ____ = ____

HOW DO YOU SAY?

Language:
_____

Hello:

Goodbye:

Please:

Thank you:

Sights	
☆☆☆☆☆	
☆☆☆☆☆	
☆☆☆☆☆	
☆☆☆☆☆	
☆☆☆☆☆	

Cities	
☆☆☆☆☆	
☆☆☆☆☆	
☆☆☆☆☆	
☆☆☆☆☆	
☆☆☆☆☆	

I'll never forget:

_____
_____
_____
_____
_____

OVERALL RATING: ☆☆☆☆☆

Guinea-Bissau

Draw the flag

ARRIVED   DEPARTED

Travel buddies:

Arrived by:

Highs F/C____   Lows F/C____

Currency:

Exchange: _____ = _____

HOW DO YOU SAY?

Language:

_____

Hello: Goodbye:

Please: Thank you:

Sights	Cities
☆☆☆☆☆	☆☆☆☆☆
☆☆☆☆☆	☆☆☆☆☆
☆☆☆☆☆	☆☆☆☆☆
☆☆☆☆☆	☆☆☆☆☆
☆☆☆☆☆	☆☆☆☆☆

I'll never forget:

_____

_____

_____

_____

_____

_____

OVERALL RATING: ☆☆☆☆☆

Ivory Coast

Draw the flag

ARRIVED   DEPARTED

Travel buddies:

Arrived by:

Highs F/C_____ Lows F/C_____

Currency:

Exchange: _____ = _____

HOW DO YOU SAY?

Language:
_____

Hello:

Goodbye:

Please:

Thank you:

Sights
☆☆☆☆☆
☆☆☆☆☆
☆☆☆☆☆
☆☆☆☆☆
☆☆☆☆☆

Cities
☆☆☆☆☆
☆☆☆☆☆
☆☆☆☆☆
☆☆☆☆☆
☆☆☆☆☆

I'll never forget:
_____
_____
_____
_____
_____
_____

OVERALL RATING: ☆☆☆☆☆

Kenya

Draw the flag

ARRIVED | DEPARTED

Travel buddies:

Arrived by:

Highs F/C____ Lows F/C____

¥ € $ Currency:

Exchange: _____ = _____

HOW DO YOU SAY?

Language:

_____

Hello: Goodbye:

Please: Thank you:

Sights
☆☆☆☆☆
☆☆☆☆☆
☆☆☆☆☆
☆☆☆☆☆
☆☆☆☆☆

Cities
☆☆☆☆☆
☆☆☆☆☆
☆☆☆☆☆
☆☆☆☆☆
☆☆☆☆☆

I'll never forget:

_____

_____

_____

_____

_____

OVERALL RATING: ☆☆☆☆☆

Lesotho

Draw the flag

ARRIVED | DEPARTED

Highs F/C____ Lows F/C____

Travel buddies:

Arrived by:

Currency:

Exchange: _____ = _____

HOW DO YOU SAY?

Language:

_____

Hello:

Please:

Goodbye:

Thank you:

Sights

⭐⭐⭐⭐⭐
⭐⭐⭐⭐⭐
⭐⭐⭐⭐⭐
⭐⭐⭐⭐⭐
⭐⭐⭐⭐⭐

Cities

⭐⭐⭐⭐⭐
⭐⭐⭐⭐⭐
⭐⭐⭐⭐⭐
⭐⭐⭐⭐⭐
⭐⭐⭐⭐⭐

I'll never forget:

OVERALL RATING: ⭐⭐⭐⭐⭐

Liberia

Draw the flag

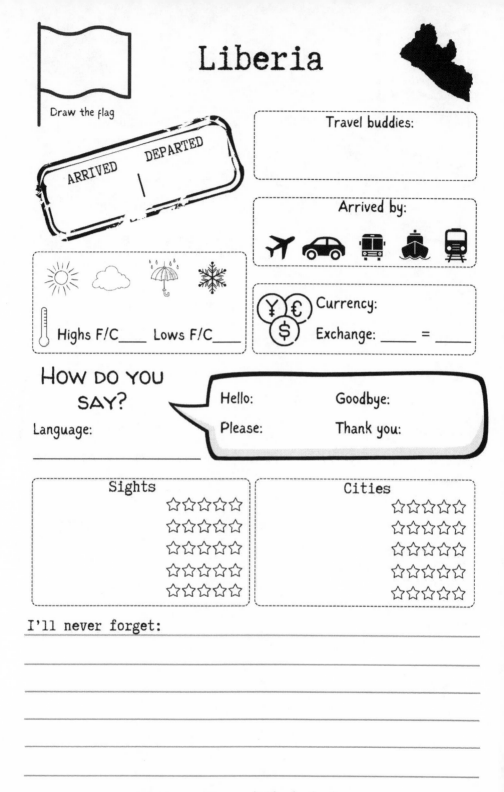

ARRIVED DEPARTED

Travel buddies:

Arrived by:

Highs F/C____ Lows F/C____

Currency:

Exchange: ____ = ____

HOW DO YOU SAY?

Language:
_____

Hello: Goodbye:

Please: Thank you:

Sights	Cities
☆☆☆☆☆	☆☆☆☆☆
☆☆☆☆☆	☆☆☆☆☆
☆☆☆☆☆	☆☆☆☆☆
☆☆☆☆☆	☆☆☆☆☆
☆☆☆☆☆	☆☆☆☆☆

I'll never forget:

_____

_____

_____

_____

_____

_____

OVERALL RATING: ☆☆☆☆☆

Libya

Draw the flag

ARRIVED   DEPARTED

Travel buddies:

Arrived by:

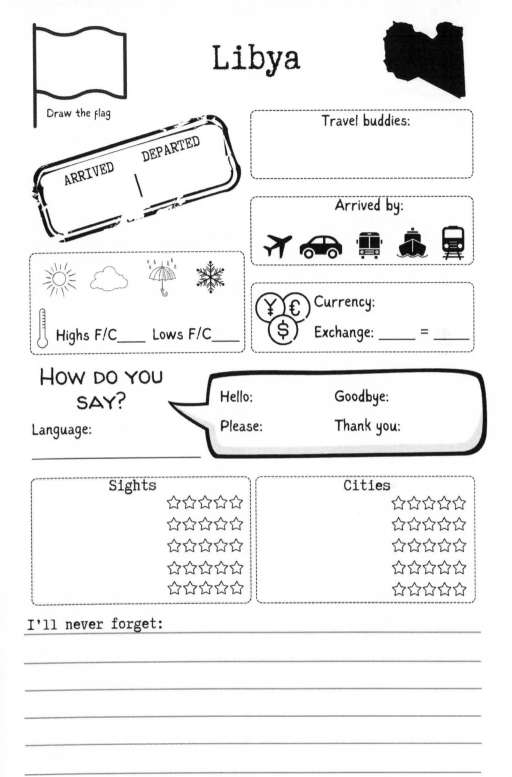

Highs F/C___ Lows F/C___

Currency:

Exchange: _____ = _____

HOW DO YOU SAY?

Language:
_____

Hello:

Please:

Goodbye:

Thank you:

Sights

Cities

I'll never forget:

_____

_____

_____

_____

_____

_____

OVERALL RATING: ☆☆☆☆☆

Madagascar

Draw the flag

ARRIVED   DEPARTED

Travel buddies:

Arrived by:

Highs F/C____ Lows F/C____

Currency:

Exchange: _____ = _____

HOW DO YOU SAY?

Language:

_____

Hello: Goodbye:

Please: Thank you:

Sights ☆☆☆☆☆
☆☆☆☆☆
☆☆☆☆☆
☆☆☆☆☆
☆☆☆☆☆

Cities ☆☆☆☆☆
☆☆☆☆☆
☆☆☆☆☆
☆☆☆☆☆
☆☆☆☆☆

I'll never forget:

OVERALL RATING: ☆☆☆☆☆

Malawi

Draw the flag

ARRIVED · DEPARTED

Highs F/C____ Lows F/C____

Travel buddies:

Arrived by:

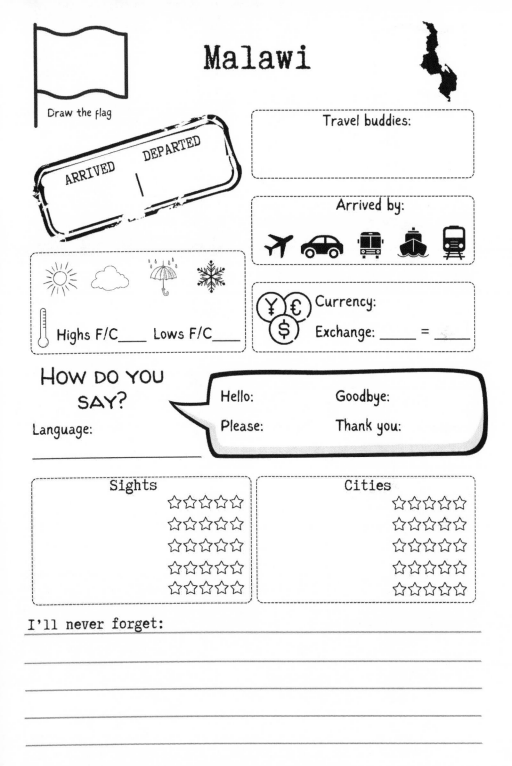

Currency:

Exchange: _____ = _____

HOW DO YOU SAY?

Language:
_____

Hello:

Goodbye:

Please:

Thank you:

Sights
☆☆☆☆☆
☆☆☆☆☆
☆☆☆☆☆
☆☆☆☆☆
☆☆☆☆☆

Cities
☆☆☆☆☆
☆☆☆☆☆
☆☆☆☆☆
☆☆☆☆☆
☆☆☆☆☆

I'll never forget:
_____
_____
_____
_____
_____

OVERALL RATING: ☆☆☆☆☆

Mali

Draw the flag

ARRIVED   DEPARTED

Travel buddies:

Arrived by:

Highs F/C____ Lows F/C____

Currency:

Exchange: _____ = _____

HOW DO YOU SAY?

Language:
_____

Hello: Goodbye:

Please: Thank you:

Sights	Cities
☆☆☆☆☆	☆☆☆☆☆
☆☆☆☆☆	☆☆☆☆☆
☆☆☆☆☆	☆☆☆☆☆
☆☆☆☆☆	☆☆☆☆☆
☆☆☆☆☆	☆☆☆☆☆

I'll never forget:

_____
_____
_____
_____
_____
_____

OVERALL RATING: ☆☆☆☆☆

Mauritania

Draw the flag

ARRIVED   DEPARTED

Travel buddies:

Arrived by:

Highs F/C____ Lows F/C____

Currency:

Exchange: _____ = _____

HOW DO YOU SAY?

Language:
_____

Hello:

Please:

Goodbye:

Thank you:

Sights

☆☆☆☆☆
☆☆☆☆☆
☆☆☆☆☆
☆☆☆☆☆
☆☆☆☆☆

Cities

☆☆☆☆☆
☆☆☆☆☆
☆☆☆☆☆
☆☆☆☆☆
☆☆☆☆☆

I'll never forget:

_____
_____
_____
_____
_____

OVERALL RATING: ☆☆☆☆☆

Mauritius

Draw the flag

ARRIVED   DEPARTED

Travel buddies:

Arrived by:

Highs F/C____ Lows F/C____

Currency:

Exchange: _____ = _____

HOW DO YOU SAY?

Language:
_____

Hello: Goodbye:

Please: Thank you:

Sights

☆☆☆☆☆
☆☆☆☆☆
☆☆☆☆☆
☆☆☆☆☆
☆☆☆☆☆

Cities

☆☆☆☆☆
☆☆☆☆☆
☆☆☆☆☆
☆☆☆☆☆
☆☆☆☆☆

I'll never forget:
_____
_____
_____
_____
_____
_____

OVERALL RATING: ☆☆☆☆☆

Morocco

Draw the flag

ARRIVED | DEPARTED

Travel buddies:

Arrived by:

Highs F/C___ Lows F/C___

Currency:

Exchange: _____ = _____

HOW DO YOU SAY?

Language:

_____

Hello:

Goodbye:

Please:

Thank you:

Sights		Cities
☆☆☆☆☆		☆☆☆☆☆
☆☆☆☆☆		☆☆☆☆☆
☆☆☆☆☆		☆☆☆☆☆
☆☆☆☆☆		☆☆☆☆☆
☆☆☆☆☆		☆☆☆☆☆

I'll never forget:

_____

_____

_____

_____

_____

OVERALL RATING: ☆☆☆☆☆

Mozambique

Draw the flag

ARRIVED   DEPARTED

Highs F/C____ Lows F/C____

Travel buddies:

Arrived by:

Currency:

Exchange: _____ = _____

HOW DO YOU SAY?

Language:

_____

Hello: Goodbye:

Please: Thank you:

Sights		Cities	
☆☆☆☆☆		☆☆☆☆☆	
☆☆☆☆☆		☆☆☆☆☆	
☆☆☆☆☆		☆☆☆☆☆	
☆☆☆☆☆		☆☆☆☆☆	
☆☆☆☆☆		☆☆☆☆☆	

I'll never forget:

_____

_____

_____

_____

_____

OVERALL RATING: ☆☆☆☆☆

Namibia

Draw the flag

ARRIVED | DEPARTED

Travel buddies:

Arrived by:

Highs F/C____ Lows F/C____

Currency:

Exchange: _____ = _____

HOW DO YOU SAY?

Language:

_____

Hello: Goodbye:

Please: Thank you:

Sights
☆☆☆☆☆
☆☆☆☆☆
☆☆☆☆☆
☆☆☆☆☆
☆☆☆☆☆

Cities
☆☆☆☆☆
☆☆☆☆☆
☆☆☆☆☆
☆☆☆☆☆
☆☆☆☆☆

I'll never forget:

_____
_____
_____
_____
_____

OVERALL RATING: ☆☆☆☆☆

Niger

Draw the flag

ARRIVED   DEPARTED

Travel buddies:

Arrived by:

Highs F/C____   Lows F/C____

Currency:

Exchange: _____ = _____

HOW DO YOU SAY?

Language:
_____

Hello: Goodbye:

Please: Thank you:

Sights
☆☆☆☆☆
☆☆☆☆☆
☆☆☆☆☆
☆☆☆☆☆
☆☆☆☆☆

Cities
☆☆☆☆☆
☆☆☆☆☆
☆☆☆☆☆
☆☆☆☆☆
☆☆☆☆☆

I'll never forget:
_____
_____
_____
_____
_____
_____

OVERALL RATING: ☆☆☆☆☆

Nigeria

Draw the flag

ARRIVED | DEPARTED

Highs F/C____ Lows F/C____

Travel buddies:

Arrived by:

Currency:

Exchange: _____ = _____

HOW DO YOU SAY?

Language:
_____

Hello:

Goodbye:

Please:

Thank you:

Sights

☆☆☆☆☆
☆☆☆☆☆
☆☆☆☆☆
☆☆☆☆☆
☆☆☆☆☆

Cities

☆☆☆☆☆
☆☆☆☆☆
☆☆☆☆☆
☆☆☆☆☆
☆☆☆☆☆

I'll never forget:

OVERALL RATING: ☆☆☆☆☆

Rwanda

Draw the flag

ARRIVED | DEPARTED

Travel buddies:

Arrived by:

Highs F/C____ Lows F/C____

Currency:

Exchange: _____ = _____

HOW DO YOU SAY?

Language:

_____

Hello:

Please:

Goodbye:

Thank you:

Sights
☆☆☆☆☆
☆☆☆☆☆
☆☆☆☆☆
☆☆☆☆☆
☆☆☆☆☆

Cities
☆☆☆☆☆
☆☆☆☆☆
☆☆☆☆☆
☆☆☆☆☆
☆☆☆☆☆

I'll never forget:

_____

_____

_____

_____

_____

OVERALL RATING: ☆☆☆☆☆

São Tomé & Príncipe

Draw the flag

ARRIVED | DEPARTED

Travel buddies:

Arrived by:

Highs F/C___ Lows F/C___

Currency:

Exchange: ___ = ___

HOW DO YOU SAY?

Language:

_____

Hello:

Please:

Goodbye:

Thank you:

Sights

☆☆☆☆☆
☆☆☆☆☆
☆☆☆☆☆
☆☆☆☆☆
☆☆☆☆☆

Cities

☆☆☆☆☆
☆☆☆☆☆
☆☆☆☆☆
☆☆☆☆☆
☆☆☆☆☆

I'll never forget:

_____
_____
_____
_____
_____

OVERALL RATING: ☆☆☆☆☆

Senegal

Draw the flag

ARRIVED   DEPARTED

Highs F/C____ Lows F/C____

Travel buddies:

Arrived by:

Currency:
Exchange: _____ = _____

HOW DO YOU SAY?

Language:
_____

Hello: Goodbye:

Please: Thank you:

Sights
☆☆☆☆☆
☆☆☆☆☆
☆☆☆☆☆
☆☆☆☆☆
☆☆☆☆☆

Cities
☆☆☆☆☆
☆☆☆☆☆
☆☆☆☆☆
☆☆☆☆☆
☆☆☆☆☆

I'll never forget:

OVERALL RATING: ☆☆☆☆☆

Seychelles

Draw the flag

ARRIVED | DEPARTED

Travel buddies:

Arrived by:

Highs F/C____ Lows F/C____

Currency:

Exchange: _____ = ____

HOW DO YOU SAY?

Language:

_____

Hello:

Please:

Goodbye:

Thank you:

Sights	
☆☆☆☆☆
☆☆☆☆☆
☆☆☆☆☆
☆☆☆☆☆
☆☆☆☆☆

Cities	
☆☆☆☆☆
☆☆☆☆☆
☆☆☆☆☆
☆☆☆☆☆
☆☆☆☆☆

I'll never forget:

_____

_____

_____

_____

_____

OVERALL RATING: ☆☆☆☆☆

Sierra Leone

Draw the flag

ARRIVED   DEPARTED

Travel buddies:

Arrived by:

Highs F/C____ Lows F/C____

Currency:

Exchange: _____ = _____

HOW DO YOU SAY?

Language:

_____

Hello: Goodbye:

Please: Thank you:

Sights		Cities	
☆☆☆☆☆		☆☆☆☆☆	
☆☆☆☆☆		☆☆☆☆☆	
☆☆☆☆☆		☆☆☆☆☆	
☆☆☆☆☆		☆☆☆☆☆	
☆☆☆☆☆		☆☆☆☆☆	

I'll never forget:

_____

_____

_____

_____

_____

OVERALL RATING: ☆☆☆☆☆

Somalia

Draw the flag

ARRIVED   DEPARTED

Highs F/C____ Lows F/C____

Travel buddies:

Arrived by:

Currency:
Exchange: _____ = _____

HOW DO YOU SAY?

Language:
_____

Hello:

Goodbye:

Please:

Thank you:

Sights	Cities
☆☆☆☆☆	☆☆☆☆☆
☆☆☆☆☆	☆☆☆☆☆
☆☆☆☆☆	☆☆☆☆☆
☆☆☆☆☆	☆☆☆☆☆
☆☆☆☆☆	☆☆☆☆☆

I'll never forget:
_____
_____
_____
_____
_____
_____

OVERALL RATING: ☆☆☆☆☆

South Africa

Draw the flag

ARRIVED   DEPARTED

Highs F/C____ Lows F/C____

Travel buddies:

Arrived by:

Currency:
Exchange: ____ = ____

HOW DO YOU SAY?

Language:
_____

Hello: Goodbye:

Please: Thank you:

Sights
☆☆☆☆☆
☆☆☆☆☆
☆☆☆☆☆
☆☆☆☆☆
☆☆☆☆☆

Cities
☆☆☆☆☆
☆☆☆☆☆
☆☆☆☆☆
☆☆☆☆☆
☆☆☆☆☆

I'll never forget:
_____
_____
_____
_____
_____

OVERALL RATING: ☆☆☆☆☆

South Sudan

Draw the flag

ARRIVED | DEPARTED

Travel buddies:

Arrived by:

Highs F/C____ Lows F/C____

Currency:

Exchange: _____ = _____

HOW DO YOU SAY?

Language:
_____

Hello:

Goodbye:

Please:

Thank you:

Sights	Cities
☆☆☆☆☆	☆☆☆☆☆
☆☆☆☆☆	☆☆☆☆☆
☆☆☆☆☆	☆☆☆☆☆
☆☆☆☆☆	☆☆☆☆☆
☆☆☆☆☆	☆☆☆☆☆

I'll never forget:

OVERALL RATING: ☆☆☆☆☆

Sudan

Draw the flag

ARRIVED DEPARTED

Travel buddies:

Arrived by:

Currency:
Exchange: _____ = _____

Highs F/C____ Lows F/C____

HOW DO YOU SAY?

Language:

_____

Hello: Goodbye:

Please: Thank you:

Sights
☆☆☆☆☆
☆☆☆☆☆
☆☆☆☆☆
☆☆☆☆☆
☆☆☆☆☆

Cities
☆☆☆☆☆
☆☆☆☆☆
☆☆☆☆☆
☆☆☆☆☆
☆☆☆☆☆

I'll never forget:

OVERALL RATING: ☆☆☆☆☆

Tanzania

Draw the flag

ARRIVED   DEPARTED

Travel buddies:

Arrived by:

Highs F/C____ Lows F/C____

Currency:

Exchange: ____ = ____

HOW DO YOU SAY?

Language:

_____

Hello:

Please:

Goodbye:

Thank you:

Sights

☆☆☆☆☆
☆☆☆☆☆
☆☆☆☆☆
☆☆☆☆☆
☆☆☆☆☆

Cities

☆☆☆☆☆
☆☆☆☆☆
☆☆☆☆☆
☆☆☆☆☆
☆☆☆☆☆

I'll never forget:

_____

_____

_____

_____

_____

OVERALL RATING: ☆☆☆☆☆

Togo

Draw the flag

ARRIVED   DEPARTED

Travel buddies:

Arrived by:

Highs F/C____ Lows F/C____

Currency:

Exchange: _____ = _____

HOW DO YOU SAY?

Language:

_____

Hello: Goodbye:

Please: Thank you:

Sights
☆☆☆☆☆
☆☆☆☆☆
☆☆☆☆☆
☆☆☆☆☆
☆☆☆☆☆

Cities
☆☆☆☆☆
☆☆☆☆☆
☆☆☆☆☆
☆☆☆☆☆
☆☆☆☆☆

I'll never forget:

OVERALL RATING: ☆☆☆☆☆

Tunisia

Draw the flag

ARRIVED | DEPARTED

Travel buddies:

Arrived by:

Highs F/C____ Lows F/C____

Currency:

Exchange: ____ = ____

HOW DO YOU SAY?

Language:
_____

Hello: Goodbye:

Please: Thank you:

Sights
☆☆☆☆☆
☆☆☆☆☆
☆☆☆☆☆
☆☆☆☆☆
☆☆☆☆☆

Cities
☆☆☆☆☆
☆☆☆☆☆
☆☆☆☆☆
☆☆☆☆☆
☆☆☆☆☆

I'll never forget:
_____
_____
_____
_____
_____
_____

OVERALL RATING: ☆☆☆☆☆

Uganda

Draw the flag

ARRIVED DEPARTED

Highs F/C____ Lows F/C____

Travel buddies:

Arrived by:

Currency:

Exchange: _____ = _____

HOW DO YOU SAY?

Language:
_____

Hello:

Goodbye:

Please:

Thank you:

Sights

☆☆☆☆☆
☆☆☆☆☆
☆☆☆☆☆
☆☆☆☆☆
☆☆☆☆☆

Cities

☆☆☆☆☆
☆☆☆☆☆
☆☆☆☆☆
☆☆☆☆☆
☆☆☆☆☆

I'll never forget:

OVERALL RATING: ☆☆☆☆☆

Zambia

Draw the flag

ARRIVED   DEPARTED

Highs F/C____   Lows F/C____

Travel buddies:

Arrived by:

Currency:

Exchange: ____ = ____

HOW DO YOU SAY?

Language:
_____

Hello:

Goodbye:

Please:

Thank you:

Sights

☆☆☆☆☆
☆☆☆☆☆
☆☆☆☆☆
☆☆☆☆☆
☆☆☆☆☆

Cities

☆☆☆☆☆
☆☆☆☆☆
☆☆☆☆☆
☆☆☆☆☆
☆☆☆☆☆

I'll never forget:
_____
_____
_____
_____
_____

OVERALL RATING: ☆☆☆☆☆

Zimbabwe

Draw the flag

ARRIVED | DEPARTED

Highs F/C____ Lows F/C____

Travel buddies:

Arrived by:

Currency:

Exchange: ____ = ____

HOW DO YOU SAY?

Language:

_____

Hello:

Please:

Goodbye:

Thank you:

Sights

☆☆☆☆☆
☆☆☆☆☆
☆☆☆☆☆
☆☆☆☆☆
☆☆☆☆☆

Cities

☆☆☆☆☆
☆☆☆☆☆
☆☆☆☆☆
☆☆☆☆☆
☆☆☆☆☆

I'll never forget:

_____

_____

_____

_____

_____

OVERALL RATING: ☆☆☆☆☆

Draw the flag

Special territory/Other

ARRIVED DEPARTED

Travel buddies:

Arrived by:

Highs F/C____ Lows F/C____

Currency:

Exchange: ____ = ____

HOW DO YOU SAY?

Language:

_____

Hello: Goodbye:

Please: Thank you:

Sights
☆☆☆☆☆
☆☆☆☆☆
☆☆☆☆☆
☆☆☆☆☆
☆☆☆☆☆

Cities
☆☆☆☆☆
☆☆☆☆☆
☆☆☆☆☆
☆☆☆☆☆
☆☆☆☆☆

I'll never forget:

OVERALL RATING: ☆☆☆☆☆

Antarctica

The only true failure would be not to explore at all.

—Ernest Shackleton

Antarctica

Draw the flag

ARRIVED | DEPARTED

Travel buddies:

Arrived by:

Highs F/C____ Lows F/C____

Currency:

Exchange: _____ = _____

HOW DO YOU SAY?

Language:
_____

Hello:

Goodbye:

Please:

Thank you:

Sights

☆☆☆☆☆
☆☆☆☆☆
☆☆☆☆☆
☆☆☆☆☆
☆☆☆☆☆

Cities

☆☆☆☆☆
☆☆☆☆☆
☆☆☆☆☆
☆☆☆☆☆
☆☆☆☆☆

I'll never forget:

_____
_____
_____
_____
_____

OVERALL RATING: ☆☆☆☆☆

Asia

No one realizes how beautiful it is to
travel until he comes home and rests his
head on his old, familiar pillow.

—Lin Yutang

Afghanistan

Draw the flag

ARRIVED   DEPARTED

Travel buddies:

Arrived by:

Highs F/C____ Lows F/C____

Currency:

Exchange: ____ = ____

HOW DO YOU SAY?

Language:
_____

Hello:

Goodbye:

Please:

Thank you:

Sights	
☆☆☆☆☆	
☆☆☆☆☆	
☆☆☆☆☆	
☆☆☆☆☆	
☆☆☆☆☆	

Cities	
☆☆☆☆☆	
☆☆☆☆☆	
☆☆☆☆☆	
☆☆☆☆☆	
☆☆☆☆☆	

I'll never forget:

OVERALL RATING: ☆☆☆☆☆

Armenia

Draw the flag

ARRIVED | DEPARTED

Highs F/C____ Lows F/C____

Travel buddies:

Arrived by:

Currency:
Exchange: _____ = _____

HOW DO YOU SAY?

Language:
_____

Hello: Goodbye:

Please: Thank you:

Sights	
☆☆☆☆☆
☆☆☆☆☆
☆☆☆☆☆
☆☆☆☆☆
☆☆☆☆☆

Cities	
☆☆☆☆☆
☆☆☆☆☆
☆☆☆☆☆
☆☆☆☆☆
☆☆☆☆☆

I'll never forget:
_____
_____
_____
_____
_____

OVERALL RATING: ☆☆☆☆☆

Azerbaijan

Draw the flag

ARRIVED | DEPARTED

Highs F/C____ Lows F/C____

Travel buddies:

Arrived by:

Currency:
Exchange: ____ = ____

HOW DO YOU SAY?

Language:
_____

Hello:

Goodbye:

Please:

Thank you:

Sights	
☆☆☆☆☆	
☆☆☆☆☆	
☆☆☆☆☆	
☆☆☆☆☆	
☆☆☆☆☆	

Cities	
☆☆☆☆☆	
☆☆☆☆☆	
☆☆☆☆☆	
☆☆☆☆☆	
☆☆☆☆☆	

I'll never forget:

_____

_____

_____

_____

_____

OVERALL RATING: ☆☆☆☆☆

Bahrain

Draw the flag

ARRIVED | DEPARTED

Travel buddies:

Arrived by:

Highs F/C____ Lows F/C____

Currency:
Exchange: _____ = _____

HOW DO YOU SAY?

Language:
_____

Hello: Goodbye:

Please: Thank you:

Sights	Cities
☆☆☆☆☆	☆☆☆☆☆
☆☆☆☆☆	☆☆☆☆☆
☆☆☆☆☆	☆☆☆☆☆
☆☆☆☆☆	☆☆☆☆☆
☆☆☆☆☆	☆☆☆☆☆

I'll never forget:

_____
_____
_____
_____
_____

OVERALL RATING: ☆☆☆☆☆

Bangladesh

Draw the flag

ARRIVED | DEPARTED

Highs F/C____ Lows F/C____

Travel buddies:

Arrived by:

Currency:

Exchange: ____ = ____

HOW DO YOU SAY?

Language:

_____

Hello:

Please:

Goodbye:

Thank you:

Sights	Cities
☆☆☆☆☆	☆☆☆☆☆
☆☆☆☆☆	☆☆☆☆☆
☆☆☆☆☆	☆☆☆☆☆
☆☆☆☆☆	☆☆☆☆☆
☆☆☆☆☆	☆☆☆☆☆

I'll never forget:

_____

_____

_____

_____

_____

_____

OVERALL RATING: ☆☆☆☆☆

Bhutan

Draw the flag

ARRIVED   DEPARTED

Travel buddies:

Arrived by:

Highs F/C____ Lows F/C____

Currency:
Exchange: ____ = ____

HOW DO YOU SAY?

Language:
_____

Hello: Goodbye:

Please: Thank you:

Sights
☆☆☆☆☆
☆☆☆☆☆
☆☆☆☆☆
☆☆☆☆☆
☆☆☆☆☆

Cities
☆☆☆☆☆
☆☆☆☆☆
☆☆☆☆☆
☆☆☆☆☆
☆☆☆☆☆

I'll never forget:

OVERALL RATING: ☆☆☆☆☆

Brunei

Draw the flag

ARRIVED DEPARTED

Highs F/C____ Lows F/C____

Travel buddies:

Arrived by:

Currency:

Exchange: ____ = ____

HOW DO YOU SAY?

Language:
_____

Hello:

Goodbye:

Please:

Thank you:

Sights	Cities
☆☆☆☆☆	☆☆☆☆☆
☆☆☆☆☆	☆☆☆☆☆
☆☆☆☆☆	☆☆☆☆☆
☆☆☆☆☆	☆☆☆☆☆
☆☆☆☆☆	☆☆☆☆☆

I'll never forget:

OVERALL RATING: ☆☆☆☆☆

Cambodia

Draw the flag

ARRIVED   DEPARTED

Travel buddies:

Arrived by:

Highs F/C____ Lows F/C____

Currency:
Exchange: _____ = _____

HOW DO YOU SAY?

Language:
_____

Hello: Goodbye:

Please: Thank you:

Sights	Cities
☆☆☆☆☆	☆☆☆☆☆
☆☆☆☆☆	☆☆☆☆☆
☆☆☆☆☆	☆☆☆☆☆
☆☆☆☆☆	☆☆☆☆☆
☆☆☆☆☆	☆☆☆☆☆

I'll never forget:

OVERALL RATING: ☆☆☆☆☆

China

Draw the flag

ARRIVED | DEPARTED

Travel buddies:

Arrived by:

Highs F/C____ Lows F/C____

Currency:
Exchange: ____ = ____

HOW DO YOU SAY?

Language:
_____

Hello: Goodbye:

Please: Thank you:

Sights
☆☆☆☆☆
☆☆☆☆☆
☆☆☆☆☆
☆☆☆☆☆
☆☆☆☆☆

Cities
☆☆☆☆☆
☆☆☆☆☆
☆☆☆☆☆
☆☆☆☆☆
☆☆☆☆☆

I'll never forget:
_____
_____
_____
_____
_____
_____

OVERALL RATING: ☆☆☆☆☆

Cyprus

Draw the flag

ARRIVED | DEPARTED

Travel buddies:

Arrived by:

Highs F/C___ Lows F/C___

Currency:

Exchange: _____ = _____

HOW DO YOU SAY?

Language:
_____

Hello:

Goodbye:

Please:

Thank you:

Sights

☆☆☆☆☆
☆☆☆☆☆
☆☆☆☆☆
☆☆☆☆☆
☆☆☆☆☆

Cities

☆☆☆☆☆
☆☆☆☆☆
☆☆☆☆☆
☆☆☆☆☆
☆☆☆☆☆

I'll never forget:
_____
_____
_____
_____
_____

OVERALL RATING: ☆☆☆☆☆

Georgia

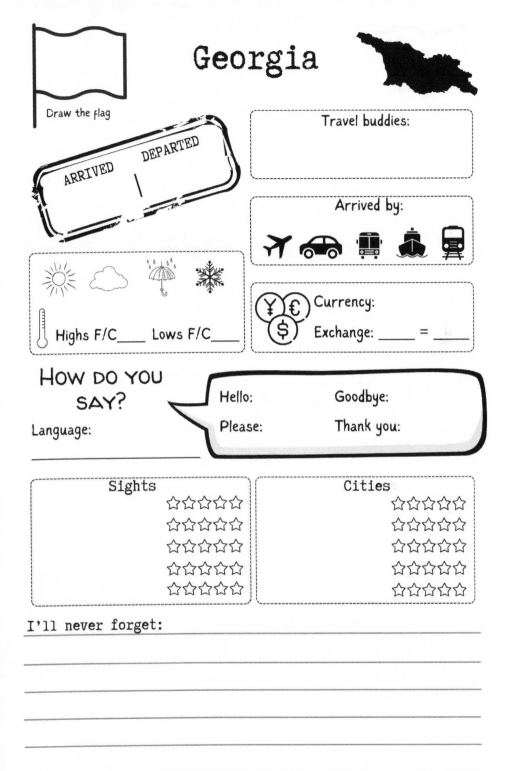

Draw the flag

ARRIVED | DEPARTED

Travel buddies:

Arrived by:

Highs F/C____ Lows F/C____

Currency:
Exchange: _____ = _____

HOW DO YOU SAY?

Language:
_____

Hello:

Goodbye:

Please:

Thank you:

Sights
☆☆☆☆☆
☆☆☆☆☆
☆☆☆☆☆
☆☆☆☆☆
☆☆☆☆☆

Cities
☆☆☆☆☆
☆☆☆☆☆
☆☆☆☆☆
☆☆☆☆☆
☆☆☆☆☆

I'll never forget:

OVERALL RATING: ☆☆☆☆☆

India

Draw the flag

ARRIVED   DEPARTED

Travel buddies:

Arrived by:

Highs F/C____ Lows F/C____

Currency:

Exchange: _____ = _____

HOW DO YOU SAY?

Language:

_____

Hello: Goodbye:

Please: Thank you:

Sights

☆☆☆☆☆
☆☆☆☆☆
☆☆☆☆☆
☆☆☆☆☆
☆☆☆☆☆

Cities

☆☆☆☆☆
☆☆☆☆☆
☆☆☆☆☆
☆☆☆☆☆
☆☆☆☆☆

I'll never forget:

_____
_____
_____
_____
_____

OVERALL RATING: ☆☆☆☆☆

Indonesia

Draw the flag

ARRIVED | DEPARTED

Travel buddies:

Arrived by:

Highs F/C____ Lows F/C____

Currency:

Exchange: ____ = ____

HOW DO YOU SAY?

Language:
_____

Hello:

Goodbye:

Please:

Thank you:

Sights

Cities

I'll never forget:

_____

_____

_____

_____

_____

_____

OVERALL RATING: ☆☆☆☆☆

Iran

Draw the flag

ARRIVED | DEPARTED

Travel buddies:

Arrived by:

Highs F/C____ Lows F/C____

Currency:

Exchange: _____ = _____

HOW DO YOU SAY?

Language:

_____

Hello:

Goodbye:

Please:

Thank you:

Sights

☆☆☆☆☆
☆☆☆☆☆
☆☆☆☆☆
☆☆☆☆☆
☆☆☆☆☆

Cities

☆☆☆☆☆
☆☆☆☆☆
☆☆☆☆☆
☆☆☆☆☆
☆☆☆☆☆

I'll never forget:

_____
_____
_____
_____
_____

OVERALL RATING: ☆☆☆☆☆

Iraq

Draw the flag

ARRIVED | DEPARTED

Travel buddies:

Arrived by:

Highs F/C____ Lows F/C____

Currency:

Exchange: _____ = _____

HOW DO YOU SAY?

Language:
_____

Hello:

Goodbye:

Please:

Thank you:

Sights
☆☆☆☆☆
☆☆☆☆☆
☆☆☆☆☆
☆☆☆☆☆
☆☆☆☆☆

Cities
☆☆☆☆☆
☆☆☆☆☆
☆☆☆☆☆
☆☆☆☆☆
☆☆☆☆☆

I'll never forget:
_____
_____
_____
_____
_____
_____

OVERALL RATING: ☆☆☆☆☆

Israel

Draw the flag

ARRIVED   DEPARTED

Travel buddies:

Arrived by:

Highs F/C____ Lows F/C____

Currency:
Exchange: _____ = _____

HOW DO YOU SAY?

Language:
_____

Hello: Goodbye:

Please: Thank you:

Sights	
☆☆☆☆☆
☆☆☆☆☆
☆☆☆☆☆
☆☆☆☆☆
☆☆☆☆☆

Cities	
☆☆☆☆☆
☆☆☆☆☆
☆☆☆☆☆
☆☆☆☆☆
☆☆☆☆☆

I'll never forget:

OVERALL RATING: ☆☆☆☆☆

Japan

Draw the flag

ARRIVED | DEPARTED

Travel buddies:

Arrived by:

Highs F/C____ Lows F/C____

Currency:

Exchange: ____ = ____

HOW DO YOU SAY?

Language:
_____

Hello:

Goodbye:

Please:

Thank you:

Sights

☆☆☆☆☆
☆☆☆☆☆
☆☆☆☆☆
☆☆☆☆☆
☆☆☆☆☆

Cities

☆☆☆☆☆
☆☆☆☆☆
☆☆☆☆☆
☆☆☆☆☆
☆☆☆☆☆

I'll never forget:
_____
_____
_____
_____
_____

OVERALL RATING: ☆☆☆☆☆

Jordan

Draw the flag

ARRIVED | DEPARTED

Travel buddies:

Arrived by:

Highs F/C____ Lows F/C____

Currency:

Exchange: ____ = ____

HOW DO YOU SAY?

Language:

_____

Hello:

Goodbye:

Please:

Thank you:

Sights

☆☆☆☆☆
☆☆☆☆☆
☆☆☆☆☆
☆☆☆☆☆
☆☆☆☆☆

Cities

☆☆☆☆☆
☆☆☆☆☆
☆☆☆☆☆
☆☆☆☆☆
☆☆☆☆☆

I'll never forget:

OVERALL RATING: ☆☆☆☆☆

Kazakhstan

Draw the flag

ARRIVED | DEPARTED

Travel buddies:

Arrived by:

Highs F/C____ Lows F/C____

Currency:

Exchange: _____ = _____

HOW DO YOU SAY?

Language:

_____

Hello:

Please:

Goodbye:

Thank you:

Sights

☆☆☆☆☆
☆☆☆☆☆
☆☆☆☆☆
☆☆☆☆☆
☆☆☆☆☆

Cities

☆☆☆☆☆
☆☆☆☆☆
☆☆☆☆☆
☆☆☆☆☆
☆☆☆☆☆

I'll never forget:

_____

_____

_____

_____

_____

OVERALL RATING: ☆☆☆☆☆

Kuwait

Draw the flag

ARRIVED DEPARTED

Travel buddies:

Arrived by:

Highs F/C____ Lows F/C____

Currency:

Exchange: ____ = ____

HOW DO YOU SAY?

Language:

_____

Hello: Goodbye:

Please: Thank you:

Sights	Cities
☆☆☆☆☆	☆☆☆☆☆
☆☆☆☆☆	☆☆☆☆☆
☆☆☆☆☆	☆☆☆☆☆
☆☆☆☆☆	☆☆☆☆☆
☆☆☆☆☆	☆☆☆☆☆

I'll never forget:

OVERALL RATING: ☆☆☆☆☆

Kyrgyzstan

Draw the flag

ARRIVED   DEPARTED

Travel buddies:

Arrived by:

Highs F/C____ Lows F/C____

Currency:

Exchange: _____ = _____

HOW DO YOU SAY?

Language:

_____

Hello: Goodbye:

Please: Thank you:

Sights	Cities
☆☆☆☆☆	☆☆☆☆☆
☆☆☆☆☆	☆☆☆☆☆
☆☆☆☆☆	☆☆☆☆☆
☆☆☆☆☆	☆☆☆☆☆
☆☆☆☆☆	☆☆☆☆☆

I'll never forget:

_____

_____

_____

_____

_____

OVERALL RATING: ☆☆☆☆☆

Laos

Draw the flag

ARRIVED DEPARTED

Travel buddies:

Arrived by:

Highs F/C____ Lows F/C____

Currency:

Exchange: _____ = _____

HOW DO YOU SAY?

Language:
_____

Hello:

Goodbye:

Please:

Thank you:

Sights
☆☆☆☆☆
☆☆☆☆☆
☆☆☆☆☆
☆☆☆☆☆
☆☆☆☆☆

Cities
☆☆☆☆☆
☆☆☆☆☆
☆☆☆☆☆
☆☆☆☆☆
☆☆☆☆☆

I'll never forget:

_____
_____
_____
_____
_____
_____

OVERALL RATING: ☆☆☆☆☆

Lebanon

Draw the flag

ARRIVED | DEPARTED

Travel buddies:

Arrived by:

Highs F/C____ Lows F/C____

Currency:

Exchange: ____ = ____

HOW DO YOU SAY?

Language:
_____

Hello:

Goodbye:

Please:

Thank you:

Sights

☆☆☆☆☆
☆☆☆☆☆
☆☆☆☆☆
☆☆☆☆☆
☆☆☆☆☆

Cities

☆☆☆☆☆
☆☆☆☆☆
☆☆☆☆☆
☆☆☆☆☆
☆☆☆☆☆

I'll never forget:
_____
_____
_____
_____
_____

OVERALL RATING: ☆☆☆☆☆

Malaysia

Draw the flag

ARRIVED | DEPARTED

Travel buddies:

Arrived by:

Highs F/C____ Lows F/C____

¥ € $ Currency:

Exchange: _____ = _____

HOW DO YOU SAY?

Language:
_____

Hello: Goodbye:

Please: Thank you:

Sights
☆☆☆☆☆
☆☆☆☆☆
☆☆☆☆☆
☆☆☆☆☆
☆☆☆☆☆

Cities
☆☆☆☆☆
☆☆☆☆☆
☆☆☆☆☆
☆☆☆☆☆
☆☆☆☆☆

I'll never forget:
_____
_____
_____
_____
_____

OVERALL RATING: ☆☆☆☆☆

Maldives

Draw the flag

ARRIVED   DEPARTED

Travel buddies:

Arrived by:

Highs F/C____   Lows F/C____

Currency:
Exchange: _____ = _____

HOW DO YOU SAY?

Language:
_____

Hello: Goodbye:

Please: Thank you:

Sights   Cities
☆☆☆☆☆   ☆☆☆☆☆
☆☆☆☆☆   ☆☆☆☆☆
☆☆☆☆☆   ☆☆☆☆☆
☆☆☆☆☆   ☆☆☆☆☆
☆☆☆☆☆   ☆☆☆☆☆

I'll never forget:
_____
_____
_____
_____
_____

OVERALL RATING: ☆☆☆☆☆

Mongolia

Draw the flag

ARRIVED   DEPARTED

Travel buddies:

Arrived by:

Highs F/C____ Lows F/C____

Currency:

Exchange: ____ = ____

HOW DO YOU SAY?

Language:
_____

Hello: Goodbye:

Please: Thank you:

Sights
☆☆☆☆☆
☆☆☆☆☆
☆☆☆☆☆
☆☆☆☆☆
☆☆☆☆☆

Cities
☆☆☆☆☆
☆☆☆☆☆
☆☆☆☆☆
☆☆☆☆☆
☆☆☆☆☆

I'll never forget:
_____
_____
_____
_____
_____

OVERALL RATING: ☆☆☆☆☆

Myanmar (Burma)

Draw the flag

ARRIVED | DEPARTED

Travel buddies:

Arrived by:

Highs F/C____ Lows F/C____

Currency:

Exchange: _____ = _____

HOW DO YOU SAY?

Language:
_____

Hello:

Goodbye:

Please:

Thank you:

Sights

☆☆☆☆☆
☆☆☆☆☆
☆☆☆☆☆
☆☆☆☆☆
☆☆☆☆☆

Cities

☆☆☆☆☆
☆☆☆☆☆
☆☆☆☆☆
☆☆☆☆☆
☆☆☆☆☆

I'll never forget:
_____
_____
_____
_____
_____

OVERALL RATING: ☆☆☆☆☆

Nepal

Draw the flag

ARRIVED | DEPARTED

Travel buddies:

Arrived by:

Highs F/C____ Lows F/C____

Currency:

Exchange: _____ = _____

HOW DO YOU SAY?

Language:

_____

Hello:

Goodbye:

Please:

Thank you:

Sights

☆☆☆☆☆
☆☆☆☆☆
☆☆☆☆☆
☆☆☆☆☆
☆☆☆☆☆

Cities

☆☆☆☆☆
☆☆☆☆☆
☆☆☆☆☆
☆☆☆☆☆
☆☆☆☆☆

I'll never forget:

_____

_____

_____

_____

_____

OVERALL RATING: ☆☆☆☆☆

North Korea

Draw the flag

ARRIVED DEPARTED

Travel buddies:

Arrived by:

Highs F/C____ Lows F/C____

Currency:

Exchange: ____ = ____

HOW DO YOU SAY?

Language:

_____

Hello:

Please:

Goodbye:

Thank you:

Sights	
☆☆☆☆☆	
☆☆☆☆☆	
☆☆☆☆☆	
☆☆☆☆☆	
☆☆☆☆☆	

Cities	
☆☆☆☆☆	
☆☆☆☆☆	
☆☆☆☆☆	
☆☆☆☆☆	
☆☆☆☆☆	

I'll never forget:

_____

_____

_____

_____

_____

OVERALL RATING: ☆☆☆☆☆

Oman

Draw the flag

ARRIVED DEPARTED

Travel buddies:

Arrived by:

Currency:

Exchange: _____ = _____

Highs F/C____ Lows F/C____

HOW DO YOU SAY?

Language:

_____

Hello:

Please:

Goodbye:

Thank you:

Sights

☆☆☆☆☆
☆☆☆☆☆
☆☆☆☆☆
☆☆☆☆☆
☆☆☆☆☆

Cities

☆☆☆☆☆
☆☆☆☆☆
☆☆☆☆☆
☆☆☆☆☆
☆☆☆☆☆

I'll never forget:

OVERALL RATING: ☆☆☆☆☆

Pakistan

Draw the flag

ARRIVED   DEPARTED

Travel buddies:

Arrived by:

Highs F/C____ Lows F/C____

Currency:

Exchange: ____ = ____

HOW DO YOU SAY?

Language:
_____

Hello:

Goodbye:

Please:

Thank you:

Sights

☆☆☆☆☆
☆☆☆☆☆
☆☆☆☆☆
☆☆☆☆☆
☆☆☆☆☆

Cities

☆☆☆☆☆
☆☆☆☆☆
☆☆☆☆☆
☆☆☆☆☆
☆☆☆☆☆

I'll never forget:
_____
_____
_____
_____
_____

OVERALL RATING: ☆☆☆☆☆

Palistine

Draw the flag

ARRIVED   DEPARTED

Travel buddies:

Arrived by:

Highs F/C____ Lows F/C____

Currency:

Exchange: ____ = ____

HOW DO YOU SAY?

Language:
_____

Hello: Goodbye:

Please: Thank you:

Sights
☆☆☆☆☆
☆☆☆☆☆
☆☆☆☆☆
☆☆☆☆☆
☆☆☆☆☆

Cities
☆☆☆☆☆
☆☆☆☆☆
☆☆☆☆☆
☆☆☆☆☆
☆☆☆☆☆

I'll never forget:
_____
_____
_____
_____
_____
_____

OVERALL RATING: ☆☆☆☆☆

Philippines

Draw the flag

ARRIVED   DEPARTED

Travel buddies:

Arrived by:

Highs F/C____ Lows F/C____

Currency:
Exchange: _____ = _____

HOW DO YOU SAY?

Language:
_____

Hello: Goodbye:

Please: Thank you:

Sights ☆☆☆☆☆
☆☆☆☆☆
☆☆☆☆☆
☆☆☆☆☆
☆☆☆☆☆

Cities ☆☆☆☆☆
☆☆☆☆☆
☆☆☆☆☆
☆☆☆☆☆
☆☆☆☆☆

I'll never forget:
_____
_____
_____
_____
_____
_____

OVERALL RATING: ☆☆☆☆☆

Qatar

Draw the flag

ARRIVED DEPARTED

Travel buddies:

Arrived by:

Highs F/C____ Lows F/C____

Currency:
Exchange: _____ = _____

HOW DO YOU SAY?

Language:
_____

Hello: Goodbye:

Please: Thank you:

Sights
☆☆☆☆☆
☆☆☆☆☆
☆☆☆☆☆
☆☆☆☆☆
☆☆☆☆☆

Cities
☆☆☆☆☆
☆☆☆☆☆
☆☆☆☆☆
☆☆☆☆☆
☆☆☆☆☆

I'll never forget:
_____
_____
_____
_____
_____

OVERALL RATING: ☆☆☆☆☆

Saudi Arabia

Draw the flag

ARRIVED | DEPARTED

Travel buddies:

Arrived by:

Highs F/C____ Lows F/C____

Currency:

Exchange: ____ = ____

HOW DO YOU SAY?

Language:
_____

Hello:

Goodbye:

Please:

Thank you:

Sights		Cities	
☆☆☆☆☆		☆☆☆☆☆	
☆☆☆☆☆		☆☆☆☆☆	
☆☆☆☆☆		☆☆☆☆☆	
☆☆☆☆☆		☆☆☆☆☆	
☆☆☆☆☆		☆☆☆☆☆	

I'll never forget:
_____
_____
_____
_____
_____

OVERALL RATING: ☆☆☆☆☆

Singapore

Draw the flag

ARRIVED DEPARTED

Travel buddies:

Arrived by:

Highs F/C___ Lows F/C___

Currency:

Exchange: ___ = ___

HOW DO YOU SAY?

Language:

_____

Hello:

Please:

Goodbye:

Thank you:

Sights	Cities
☆☆☆☆☆	☆☆☆☆☆
☆☆☆☆☆	☆☆☆☆☆
☆☆☆☆☆	☆☆☆☆☆
☆☆☆☆☆	☆☆☆☆☆
☆☆☆☆☆	☆☆☆☆☆

I'll never forget:

_____

_____

_____

_____

_____

OVERALL RATING: ☆☆☆☆☆

South Korea

Draw the flag

ARRIVED — DEPARTED

Travel buddies:

Arrived by:

Highs F/C____ Lows F/C____

Currency:

Exchange: _____ = _____

HOW DO YOU SAY?

Language:

_____

Hello:

Please:

Goodbye:

Thank you:

Sights

☆☆☆☆☆
☆☆☆☆☆
☆☆☆☆☆
☆☆☆☆☆
☆☆☆☆☆

Cities

☆☆☆☆☆
☆☆☆☆☆
☆☆☆☆☆
☆☆☆☆☆
☆☆☆☆☆

I'll never forget:

OVERALL RATING: ☆☆☆☆☆

Sri Lanka

Draw the flag

ARRIVED   DEPARTED

Highs F/C____ Lows F/C____

Travel buddies:

Arrived by:

Currency:
Exchange: _____ = _____

HOW DO YOU SAY?

Language:
_____

Hello: Goodbye:

Please: Thank you:

Sights ☆☆☆☆☆
☆☆☆☆☆
☆☆☆☆☆
☆☆☆☆☆
☆☆☆☆☆

Cities ☆☆☆☆☆
☆☆☆☆☆
☆☆☆☆☆
☆☆☆☆☆
☆☆☆☆☆

I'll never forget:

OVERALL RATING: ☆☆☆☆☆

Syria

Draw the flag

ARRIVED   DEPARTED

Travel buddies:

Arrived by:

Highs F/C____ Lows F/C____

Currency:

Exchange: ____ = ____

HOW DO YOU SAY?

Language:
_____

Hello: Goodbye:

Please: Thank you:

Sights

☆☆☆☆☆
☆☆☆☆☆
☆☆☆☆☆
☆☆☆☆☆
☆☆☆☆☆

Cities

☆☆☆☆☆
☆☆☆☆☆
☆☆☆☆☆
☆☆☆☆☆
☆☆☆☆☆

I'll never forget:

OVERALL RATING: ☆☆☆☆☆

Tajikistan

Draw the flag

ARRIVED | DEPARTED

Travel buddies:

Arrived by:

Highs F/C____ Lows F/C____

Currency:

Exchange: ____ = ____

HOW DO YOU SAY?

Language:
_____

Hello: Goodbye:

Please: Thank you:

Sights
☆☆☆☆☆
☆☆☆☆☆
☆☆☆☆☆
☆☆☆☆☆
☆☆☆☆☆

Cities
☆☆☆☆☆
☆☆☆☆☆
☆☆☆☆☆
☆☆☆☆☆
☆☆☆☆☆

I'll never forget:

_____

_____

_____

_____

_____

OVERALL RATING: ☆☆☆☆☆

Thailand

Draw the flag

ARRIVED | DEPARTED

Travel buddies:

Arrived by:

Highs F/C___ Lows F/C___

Currency:
Exchange: ___ = ___

HOW DO YOU SAY?

Language:
_____

Hello:

Goodbye:

Please:

Thank you:

Sights
☆☆☆☆☆
☆☆☆☆☆
☆☆☆☆☆
☆☆☆☆☆
☆☆☆☆☆

Cities
☆☆☆☆☆
☆☆☆☆☆
☆☆☆☆☆
☆☆☆☆☆
☆☆☆☆☆

I'll never forget:
_____
_____
_____
_____
_____

OVERALL RATING: ☆☆☆☆☆

Timor-Leste

Draw the flag

ARRIVED | DEPARTED

Travel buddies:

Arrived by:

Highs F/C____ Lows F/C____

Currency:

Exchange: _____ = _____

HOW DO YOU SAY?

Language:
_____

Hello:

Goodbye:

Please:

Thank you:

Sights		Cities	
☆☆☆☆☆		☆☆☆☆☆	
☆☆☆☆☆		☆☆☆☆☆	
☆☆☆☆☆		☆☆☆☆☆	
☆☆☆☆☆		☆☆☆☆☆	
☆☆☆☆☆		☆☆☆☆☆	

I'll never forget:
_____
_____
_____
_____
_____

OVERALL RATING: ☆☆☆☆☆

Turkey

Draw the flag

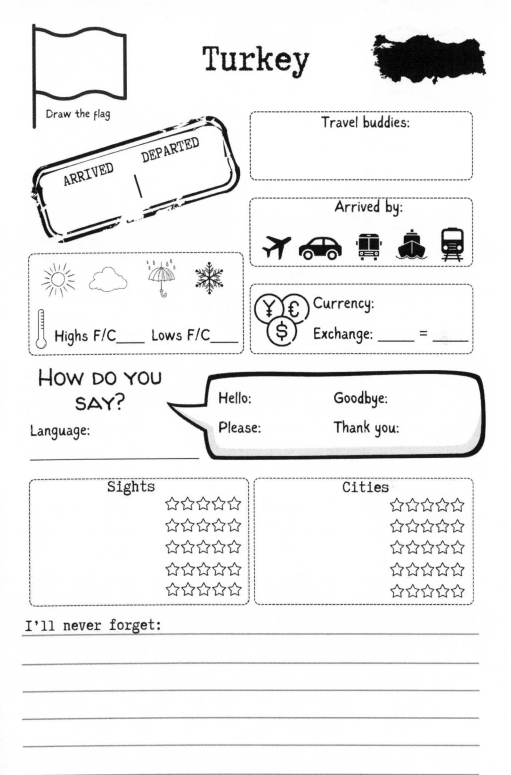

ARRIVED   DEPARTED

Travel buddies:

Arrived by:

Highs F/C____   Lows F/C____

Currency:

Exchange: ____ = ____

HOW DO YOU SAY?

Language:
_____

Hello: Goodbye:

Please: Thank you:

Sights	Cities
☆☆☆☆☆	☆☆☆☆☆
☆☆☆☆☆	☆☆☆☆☆
☆☆☆☆☆	☆☆☆☆☆
☆☆☆☆☆	☆☆☆☆☆
☆☆☆☆☆	☆☆☆☆☆

I'll never forget:
_____
_____
_____
_____
_____
_____

OVERALL RATING: ☆☆☆☆☆

Turkemenistan

Draw the flag

ARRIVED DEPARTED

Travel buddies:

Arrived by:

Highs F/C____ Lows F/C____

Currency:

Exchange: ____ = ____

HOW DO YOU SAY?

Language:
_____

Hello:

Goodbye:

Please:

Thank you:

Sights

☆☆☆☆☆
☆☆☆☆☆
☆☆☆☆☆
☆☆☆☆☆
☆☆☆☆☆

Cities

☆☆☆☆☆
☆☆☆☆☆
☆☆☆☆☆
☆☆☆☆☆
☆☆☆☆☆

I'll never forget:

_____
_____
_____
_____
_____

OVERALL RATING: ☆☆☆☆☆

United Arab Emirates

Draw the flag

ARRIVED   DEPARTED

Travel buddies:

Arrived by:

Highs F/C____ Lows F/C____

Currency:

Exchange: _____ = _____

HOW DO YOU SAY?

Language:
_____

Hello:

Goodbye:

Please:

Thank you:

Sights
☆☆☆☆☆
☆☆☆☆☆
☆☆☆☆☆
☆☆☆☆☆
☆☆☆☆☆

Cities
☆☆☆☆☆
☆☆☆☆☆
☆☆☆☆☆
☆☆☆☆☆
☆☆☆☆☆

I'll never forget:
_____
_____
_____
_____
_____

OVERALL RATING: ☆☆☆☆☆

Uzbekistan

Draw the flag

ARRIVED — DEPARTED

Travel buddies:

Arrived by:

Highs F/C____ Lows F/C____

Currency:

Exchange: _____ = _____

HOW DO YOU SAY?

Language:
_____

Hello:

Goodbye:

Please:

Thank you:

Sights

☆☆☆☆☆
☆☆☆☆☆
☆☆☆☆☆
☆☆☆☆☆
☆☆☆☆☆

Cities

☆☆☆☆☆
☆☆☆☆☆
☆☆☆☆☆
☆☆☆☆☆
☆☆☆☆☆

I'll never forget:

_____

_____

_____

_____

_____

OVERALL RATING: ☆☆☆☆☆

Vietnam

Draw the flag

ARRIVED | DEPARTED

Travel buddies:

Arrived by:

Highs F/C____ Lows F/C____

Currency:
Exchange: ____ = ____

HOW DO YOU SAY?

Language:
_____

Hello:

Goodbye:

Please:

Thank you:

Sights	Cities
☆☆☆☆☆	☆☆☆☆☆
☆☆☆☆☆	☆☆☆☆☆
☆☆☆☆☆	☆☆☆☆☆
☆☆☆☆☆	☆☆☆☆☆
☆☆☆☆☆	☆☆☆☆☆

I'll never forget:

_____
_____
_____
_____
_____

OVERALL RATING: ☆☆☆☆☆

Yemen

Draw the flag

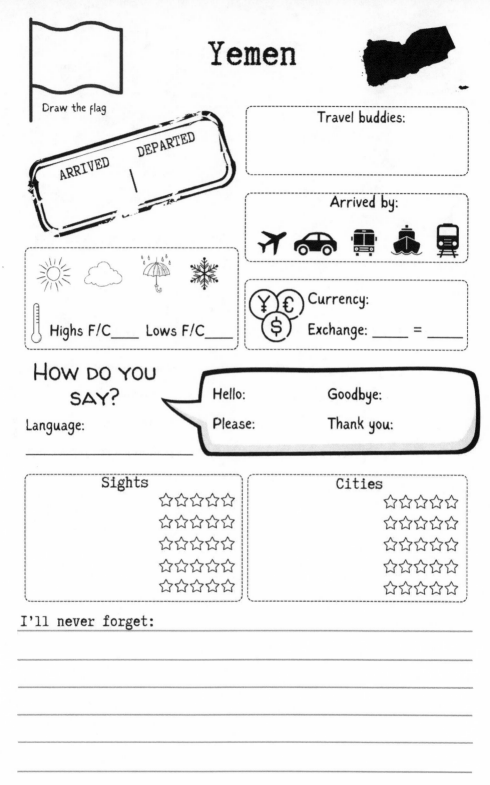

ARRIVED | DEPARTED

Travel buddies:

Arrived by:

Highs F/C____ Lows F/C____

Currency:

Exchange: _____ = _____

HOW DO YOU SAY?

Language:

_____

Hello:

Please:

Goodbye:

Thank you:

Sights	
☆☆☆☆☆	
☆☆☆☆☆	
☆☆☆☆☆	
☆☆☆☆☆	
☆☆☆☆☆	

Cities	
☆☆☆☆☆	
☆☆☆☆☆	
☆☆☆☆☆	
☆☆☆☆☆	
☆☆☆☆☆	

I'll never forget:

OVERALL RATING: ☆☆☆☆☆

Draw the flag

Special territory/Other

ARRIVED | DEPARTED

Travel buddies:

Arrived by:

Highs F/C____ Lows F/C____

Currency:
Exchange: ____ = ____

HOW DO YOU SAY?

Language:

_____

Hello:

Please:

Goodbye:

Thank you:

Sights	
☆☆☆☆☆	
☆☆☆☆☆	
☆☆☆☆☆	
☆☆☆☆☆	
☆☆☆☆☆	

Cities	
☆☆☆☆☆	
☆☆☆☆☆	
☆☆☆☆☆	
☆☆☆☆☆	
☆☆☆☆☆	

I'll never forget:

_____

_____

_____

_____

_____

OVERALL RATING: ☆☆☆☆☆

Australia and Oceania

I'm going on an adventure.

—J. R. R. Tolkien

Australia

Draw the flag

ARRIVED | DEPARTED

Travel buddies:

Arrived by:

Highs F/C____ Lows F/C____

Currency:

Exchange: ____ = ____

HOW DO YOU SAY?

Language:

_____

Hello:

Goodbye:

Please:

Thank you:

Sights	Cities
☆☆☆☆☆	☆☆☆☆☆
☆☆☆☆☆	☆☆☆☆☆
☆☆☆☆☆	☆☆☆☆☆
☆☆☆☆☆	☆☆☆☆☆
☆☆☆☆☆	☆☆☆☆☆

I'll never forget:

_____

_____

_____

_____

_____

OVERALL RATING: ☆☆☆☆☆

Fiji

Draw the flag

ARRIVED   DEPARTED

Highs F/C____ Lows F/C____

Travel buddies:

Arrived by:

Currency:

Exchange: ____ = ____

HOW DO YOU SAY?

Language:
_____

Hello: Goodbye:

Please: Thank you:

Sights

☆☆☆☆☆
☆☆☆☆☆
☆☆☆☆☆
☆☆☆☆☆
☆☆☆☆☆

Cities

☆☆☆☆☆
☆☆☆☆☆
☆☆☆☆☆
☆☆☆☆☆
☆☆☆☆☆

I'll never forget:
_____
_____
_____
_____
_____
_____
_____

OVERALL RATING: ☆☆☆☆☆

Kiribati

Draw the flag

ARRIVED   DEPARTED

Travel buddies:

Arrived by:

Highs F/C___ Lows F/C___

Currency:

Exchange: _____ = _____

HOW DO YOU SAY?

Language:

_____

Hello:

Please:

Goodbye:

Thank you:

Sights	Cities
☆☆☆☆☆	☆☆☆☆☆
☆☆☆☆☆	☆☆☆☆☆
☆☆☆☆☆	☆☆☆☆☆
☆☆☆☆☆	☆☆☆☆☆
☆☆☆☆☆	☆☆☆☆☆

I'll never forget:

OVERALL RATING: ☆☆☆☆☆

Marshall Islands

Draw the flag

ARRIVED | DEPARTED

Highs F/C____ Lows F/C____

Travel buddies:

Arrived by:

Currency:

Exchange: ____ = ____

HOW DO YOU SAY?

Language:
_____

Hello:

Goodbye:

Please:

Thank you:

Sights

☆☆☆☆☆
☆☆☆☆☆
☆☆☆☆☆
☆☆☆☆☆
☆☆☆☆☆

Cities

☆☆☆☆☆
☆☆☆☆☆
☆☆☆☆☆
☆☆☆☆☆
☆☆☆☆☆

I'll never forget:
_____
_____
_____
_____
_____
_____

OVERALL RATING: ☆☆☆☆☆

Micronesia

Draw the flag

ARRIVED   DEPARTED

Travel buddies:

Arrived by:

Highs F/C_____ Lows F/C_____

Currency:

Exchange: _____ = _____

HOW DO YOU SAY?

Language:
_____

Hello: Goodbye:

Please: Thank you:

Sights	Cities
☆☆☆☆☆	☆☆☆☆☆
☆☆☆☆☆	☆☆☆☆☆
☆☆☆☆☆	☆☆☆☆☆
☆☆☆☆☆	☆☆☆☆☆
☆☆☆☆☆	☆☆☆☆☆

I'll never forget:

_____

_____

_____

_____

_____

OVERALL RATING: ☆☆☆☆☆

Nauru

Draw the flag

ARRIVED — DEPARTED

Travel buddies:

Arrived by:

Highs F/C____ Lows F/C____

Currency:
Exchange: ____ = ____

HOW DO YOU SAY?

Language:
_____

Hello: Goodbye:

Please: Thank you:

Sights
☆☆☆☆☆
☆☆☆☆☆
☆☆☆☆☆
☆☆☆☆☆
☆☆☆☆☆

Cities
☆☆☆☆☆
☆☆☆☆☆
☆☆☆☆☆
☆☆☆☆☆
☆☆☆☆☆

I'll never forget:
_____
_____
_____
_____
_____
_____

OVERALL RATING: ☆☆☆☆☆

New Zealand

Draw the flag

ARRIVED   DEPARTED

Travel buddies:

Arrived by:

Highs F/C___ Lows F/C___

Currency:

Exchange: _____ = _____

HOW DO YOU SAY?

Language:
_____

Hello:

Goodbye:

Please:

Thank you:

Sights		Cities	
☆☆☆☆☆		☆☆☆☆☆	
☆☆☆☆☆		☆☆☆☆☆	
☆☆☆☆☆		☆☆☆☆☆	
☆☆☆☆☆		☆☆☆☆☆	
☆☆☆☆☆		☆☆☆☆☆	

I'll never forget:

_____

_____

_____

_____

_____

OVERALL RATING: ☆☆☆☆☆

Palau

Draw the flag

ARRIVED | DEPARTED

Highs F/C____ Lows F/C____

Travel buddies:

Arrived by:

Currency:
Exchange: _____ = _____

HOW DO YOU SAY?

Language:
_____

Hello: Goodbye:

Please: Thank you:

Sights
☆☆☆☆☆
☆☆☆☆☆
☆☆☆☆☆
☆☆☆☆☆
☆☆☆☆☆

Cities
☆☆☆☆☆
☆☆☆☆☆
☆☆☆☆☆
☆☆☆☆☆
☆☆☆☆☆

I'll never forget:
_____
_____
_____
_____
_____
_____

OVERALL RATING: ☆☆☆☆☆

Papau New Guinea

Draw the flag

ARRIVED   DEPARTED

Travel buddies:

Arrived by:

Highs F/C____ Lows F/C____

Currency:

Exchange: ____ = ____

HOW DO YOU SAY?

Language:
_____

Hello:

Goodbye:

Please:

Thank you:

Sights

☆☆☆☆☆
☆☆☆☆☆
☆☆☆☆☆
☆☆☆☆☆
☆☆☆☆☆

Cities

☆☆☆☆☆
☆☆☆☆☆
☆☆☆☆☆
☆☆☆☆☆
☆☆☆☆☆

I'll never forget:

_____
_____
_____
_____
_____

OVERALL RATING: ☆☆☆☆☆

Samoa

Draw the flag

ARRIVED | DEPARTED

Travel buddies:

Arrived by:

Highs F/C___ Lows F/C___

Currency:

Exchange: ____ = ____

HOW DO YOU SAY?

Language:

_____

Hello:

Please:

Goodbye:

Thank you:

Sights

☆☆☆☆☆
☆☆☆☆☆
☆☆☆☆☆
☆☆☆☆☆
☆☆☆☆☆

Cities

☆☆☆☆☆
☆☆☆☆☆
☆☆☆☆☆
☆☆☆☆☆
☆☆☆☆☆

I'll never forget:

_____
_____
_____
_____
_____

OVERALL RATING: ☆☆☆☆☆

Solomon Islands

Draw the flag

ARRIVED | DEPARTED

Travel buddies:

Arrived by:

Highs F/C____ Lows F/C____

Currency: _____
Exchange: _____ = _____

HOW DO YOU SAY?

Language:
_____

Hello:

Please:

Goodbye:

Thank you:

Sights
☆☆☆☆☆
☆☆☆☆☆
☆☆☆☆☆
☆☆☆☆☆
☆☆☆☆☆

Cities
☆☆☆☆☆
☆☆☆☆☆
☆☆☆☆☆
☆☆☆☆☆
☆☆☆☆☆

I'll never forget:
_____
_____
_____
_____
_____

OVERALL RATING: ☆☆☆☆☆

Tonga

Draw the flag

ARRIVED | DEPARTED

Highs F/C_____ Lows F/C_____

Travel buddies:

Arrived by:

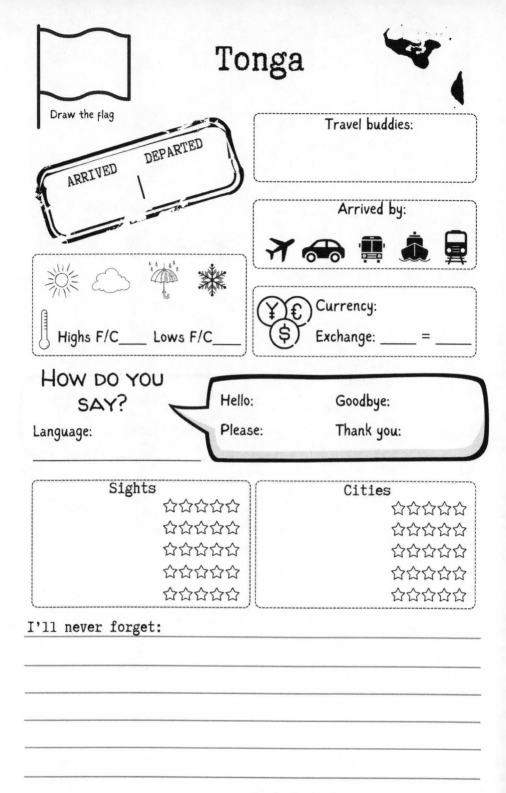

Currency:

Exchange: _____ = _____

HOW DO YOU SAY?

Language:
_____

Hello:

Goodbye:

Please:

Thank you:

Sights
☆☆☆☆☆
☆☆☆☆☆
☆☆☆☆☆
☆☆☆☆☆
☆☆☆☆☆

Cities
☆☆☆☆☆
☆☆☆☆☆
☆☆☆☆☆
☆☆☆☆☆
☆☆☆☆☆

I'll never forget:

_____
_____
_____
_____
_____
_____

OVERALL RATING: ☆☆☆☆☆

Tuvalu

Draw the flag

ARRIVED | DEPARTED

Travel buddies:

Arrived by:

Highs F/C____ Lows F/C____

Currency:

Exchange: _____ = _____

HOW DO YOU SAY?

Language:
_____

Hello:

Goodbye:

Please:

Thank you:

Sights

☆☆☆☆☆
☆☆☆☆☆
☆☆☆☆☆
☆☆☆☆☆
☆☆☆☆☆

Cities

☆☆☆☆☆
☆☆☆☆☆
☆☆☆☆☆
☆☆☆☆☆
☆☆☆☆☆

I'll never forget:

_____
_____
_____
_____
_____

OVERALL RATING: ☆☆☆☆☆

Vanuatu

Draw the flag

ARRIVED | DEPARTED

Travel buddies:

Arrived by:

Highs F/C____ Lows F/C____

Currency:
Exchange: _____ = _____

HOW DO YOU SAY?

Language:
_____

Hello:

Goodbye:

Please:

Thank you:

Sights
☆☆☆☆☆
☆☆☆☆☆
☆☆☆☆☆
☆☆☆☆☆
☆☆☆☆☆

Cities
☆☆☆☆☆
☆☆☆☆☆
☆☆☆☆☆
☆☆☆☆☆
☆☆☆☆☆

I'll never forget:

_____
_____
_____
_____
_____

OVERALL RATING: ☆☆☆☆☆

Draw the flag

Special territory/Other

ARRIVED | DEPARTED

Travel buddies:

Arrived by:

Highs F/C_____ Lows F/C_____

Currency:

Exchange: _____ = _____

HOW DO YOU SAY?

Language:

_____

Hello:

Please:

Goodbye:

Thank you:

Sights

☆☆☆☆☆
☆☆☆☆☆
☆☆☆☆☆
☆☆☆☆☆
☆☆☆☆☆

Cities

☆☆☆☆☆
☆☆☆☆☆
☆☆☆☆☆
☆☆☆☆☆
☆☆☆☆☆

I'll never forget:

OVERALL RATING: ☆☆☆☆☆

Europe

The real voyage of discovery is not in seeking new landscapes but in having new eyes, in seeing the universe with the eyes of another.

—Marcel Proust

Albania

Draw the flag

ARRIVED | DEPARTED

Travel buddies:

Arrived by:
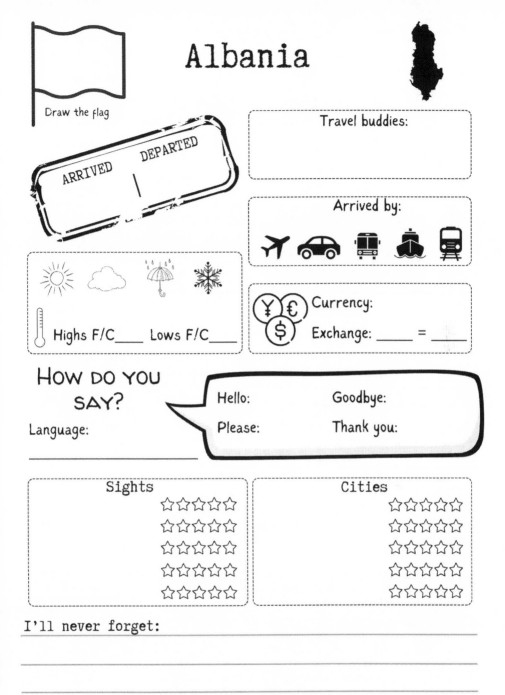

Highs F/C____ Lows F/C____

Currency:
Exchange: _____ = _____

HOW DO YOU SAY?

Language:
_____

Hello:

Goodbye:

Please:

Thank you:

Sights
☆☆☆☆☆
☆☆☆☆☆
☆☆☆☆☆
☆☆☆☆☆
☆☆☆☆☆

Cities
☆☆☆☆☆
☆☆☆☆☆
☆☆☆☆☆
☆☆☆☆☆
☆☆☆☆☆

I'll never forget:
_____
_____
_____
_____
_____

OVERALL RATING: ☆☆☆☆☆

Andorra

Draw the flag

ARRIVED | DEPARTED

Travel buddies:

Arrived by:

Highs F/C____ Lows F/C____

Currency:

Exchange: ____ = ____

HOW DO YOU SAY?

Language:
_____

Hello:

Goodbye:

Please:

Thank you:

Sights
☆☆☆☆☆
☆☆☆☆☆
☆☆☆☆☆
☆☆☆☆☆
☆☆☆☆☆

Cities
☆☆☆☆☆
☆☆☆☆☆
☆☆☆☆☆
☆☆☆☆☆
☆☆☆☆☆

I'll never forget:
_____
_____
_____
_____
_____
_____

OVERALL RATING: ☆☆☆☆☆

Austria

Draw the flag

ARRIVED   DEPARTED

Travel buddies:

Arrived by:

Highs F/C____ Lows F/C____

Currency:

Exchange: ____ = ____

HOW DO YOU SAY?

Language:

_____

Hello:

Please:

Goodbye:

Thank you:

Sights		Cities	
☆☆☆☆☆		☆☆☆☆☆	
☆☆☆☆☆		☆☆☆☆☆	
☆☆☆☆☆		☆☆☆☆☆	
☆☆☆☆☆		☆☆☆☆☆	
☆☆☆☆☆		☆☆☆☆☆	

I'll never forget:

_____

_____

_____

_____

_____

OVERALL RATING: ☆☆☆☆☆

Belarus

Draw the flag

ARRIVED | DEPARTED

Travel buddies:

Arrived by:

Highs F/C____ Lows F/C____

Currency:

Exchange: _____ = _____

HOW DO YOU SAY?

Language:
_____

Hello: Goodbye:

Please: Thank you:

Sights
☆☆☆☆☆
☆☆☆☆☆
☆☆☆☆☆
☆☆☆☆☆
☆☆☆☆☆

Cities
☆☆☆☆☆
☆☆☆☆☆
☆☆☆☆☆
☆☆☆☆☆
☆☆☆☆☆

I'll never forget:
_____
_____
_____
_____
_____
_____

OVERALL RATING: ☆☆☆☆☆

Belgium

Draw the flag

ARRIVED | DEPARTED

Travel buddies:

Arrived by:

Highs F/C____ Lows F/C____

Currency:

Exchange: _____ = _____

HOW DO YOU SAY?

Language:
_____

Hello:

Goodbye:

Please:

Thank you:

Sights
☆☆☆☆☆
☆☆☆☆☆
☆☆☆☆☆
☆☆☆☆☆
☆☆☆☆☆

Cities
☆☆☆☆☆
☆☆☆☆☆
☆☆☆☆☆
☆☆☆☆☆
☆☆☆☆☆

I'll never forget:
_____
_____
_____
_____
_____

OVERALL RATING: ☆☆☆☆☆

Bosnia and Herzegovina

Draw the flag

ARRIVED | DEPARTED

Travel buddies:

Arrived by:

Highs F/C____ Lows F/C____

Currency:

Exchange: ____ = ____

HOW DO YOU SAY?

Language:
_____

Hello:

Goodbye:

Please:

Thank you:

Sights
☆☆☆☆☆
☆☆☆☆☆
☆☆☆☆☆
☆☆☆☆☆
☆☆☆☆☆

Cities
☆☆☆☆☆
☆☆☆☆☆
☆☆☆☆☆
☆☆☆☆☆
☆☆☆☆☆

I'll never forget:

OVERALL RATING: ☆☆☆☆☆

Bulgaria

Draw the flag

ARRIVED DEPARTED

Travel buddies:

Arrived by:

Highs F/C____ Lows F/C____

Currency:
Exchange: _____ = _____

HOW DO YOU SAY?

Language:
_____

Hello:
Please:

Goodbye:
Thank you:

Sights
☆☆☆☆☆
☆☆☆☆☆
☆☆☆☆☆
☆☆☆☆☆
☆☆☆☆☆

Cities
☆☆☆☆☆
☆☆☆☆☆
☆☆☆☆☆
☆☆☆☆☆
☆☆☆☆☆

I'll never forget:
_____
_____
_____
_____
_____

OVERALL RATING: ☆☆☆☆☆

Croatia

Draw the flag

ARRIVED | DEPARTED

Highs F/C____ Lows F/C____

Travel buddies:

Arrived by:

Currency:
Exchange: ____ = ____

HOW DO YOU SAY?

Language:
_____

Hello: Goodbye:

Please: Thank you:

Sights
☆☆☆☆☆
☆☆☆☆☆
☆☆☆☆☆
☆☆☆☆☆
☆☆☆☆☆

Cities
☆☆☆☆☆
☆☆☆☆☆
☆☆☆☆☆
☆☆☆☆☆
☆☆☆☆☆

I'll never forget:
_____
_____
_____
_____
_____
_____
_____

OVERALL RATING: ☆☆☆☆☆

Czech Republic

Draw the flag

ARRIVED | DEPARTED

Travel buddies:

Arrived by:

Highs F/C____ Lows F/C____

Currency:

Exchange: _____ = _____

HOW DO YOU SAY?

Language:
_____

Hello:

Goodbye:

Please:

Thank you:

Sights

☆☆☆☆☆
☆☆☆☆☆
☆☆☆☆☆
☆☆☆☆☆
☆☆☆☆☆

Cities

☆☆☆☆☆
☆☆☆☆☆
☆☆☆☆☆
☆☆☆☆☆
☆☆☆☆☆

I'll never forget:

_____

_____

_____

_____

_____

OVERALL RATING: ☆☆☆☆☆

Denmark

Draw the flag

ARRIVED | DEPARTED

Travel buddies:

Arrived by:

Highs F/C____ Lows F/C____

Currency:

Exchange: ____ = ____

HOW DO YOU SAY?

Language:
_____

Hello:

Goodbye:

Please:

Thank you:

Sights

☆☆☆☆☆
☆☆☆☆☆
☆☆☆☆☆
☆☆☆☆☆
☆☆☆☆☆

Cities

☆☆☆☆☆
☆☆☆☆☆
☆☆☆☆☆
☆☆☆☆☆
☆☆☆☆☆

I'll never forget:

OVERALL RATING: ☆☆☆☆☆

Estonia

Draw the flag

ARRIVED | DEPARTED

Travel buddies:

Arrived by:

Highs F/C____ Lows F/C____

Currency:

Exchange: ____ = ____

HOW DO YOU SAY?

Language:
_____

Hello:

Goodbye:

Please:

Thank you:

Sights	Cities
☆☆☆☆☆	☆☆☆☆☆
☆☆☆☆☆	☆☆☆☆☆
☆☆☆☆☆	☆☆☆☆☆
☆☆☆☆☆	☆☆☆☆☆
☆☆☆☆☆	☆☆☆☆☆

I'll never forget:

_____

_____

_____

_____

_____

OVERALL RATING: ☆☆☆☆☆

Finland

Draw the flag

ARRIVED | DEPARTED

Travel buddies:

Arrived by:

Highs F/C_____ Lows F/C_____

Currency:

Exchange: _____ = _____

HOW DO YOU SAY?

Language:

_____

Hello:

Goodbye:

Please:

Thank you:

Sights

☆☆☆☆☆
☆☆☆☆☆
☆☆☆☆☆
☆☆☆☆☆
☆☆☆☆☆

Cities

☆☆☆☆☆
☆☆☆☆☆
☆☆☆☆☆
☆☆☆☆☆
☆☆☆☆☆

I'll never forget:

_____
_____
_____
_____
_____
_____

OVERALL RATING: ☆☆☆☆☆

France

Draw the flag

ARRIVED   DEPARTED

Travel buddies:

Arrived by:

Highs F/C____ Lows F/C____

Currency:

Exchange: _____ = _____

HOW DO YOU SAY?

Language:

_____

Hello:

Please:

Goodbye:

Thank you:

Sights	Cities
☆☆☆☆☆	☆☆☆☆☆
☆☆☆☆☆	☆☆☆☆☆
☆☆☆☆☆	☆☆☆☆☆
☆☆☆☆☆	☆☆☆☆☆
☆☆☆☆☆	☆☆☆☆☆

I'll never forget:

_____

_____

_____

_____

_____

OVERALL RATING: ☆☆☆☆☆

Germany

Draw the flag

ARRIVED | DEPARTED

Travel buddies:

Arrived by:

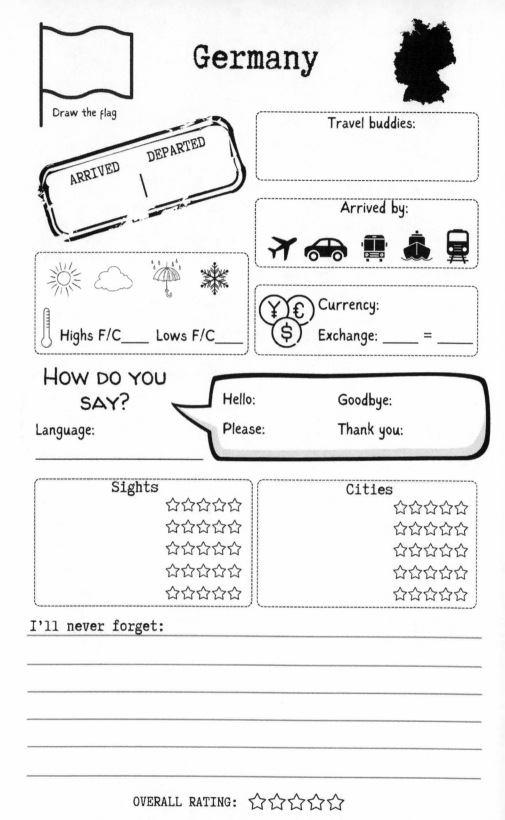

Highs F/C___ Lows F/C___

Currency:

Exchange: ___ = ___

HOW DO YOU SAY?

Language:
_____

Hello:

Please:

Goodbye:

Thank you:

Sights

☆☆☆☆☆
☆☆☆☆☆
☆☆☆☆☆
☆☆☆☆☆
☆☆☆☆☆

Cities

☆☆☆☆☆
☆☆☆☆☆
☆☆☆☆☆
☆☆☆☆☆
☆☆☆☆☆

I'll never forget:

OVERALL RATING: ☆☆☆☆☆

Greece

Draw the flag

ARRIVED | DEPARTED

Travel buddies:

Arrived by:

Highs F/C___ Lows F/C___

Currency:
Exchange: ___ = ___

HOW DO YOU SAY?

Language:
_____

Hello:

Goodbye:

Please:

Thank you:

Sights ☆☆☆☆☆ ☆☆☆☆☆ ☆☆☆☆☆ ☆☆☆☆☆ ☆☆☆☆☆

Cities ☆☆☆☆☆ ☆☆☆☆☆ ☆☆☆☆☆ ☆☆☆☆☆ ☆☆☆☆☆

I'll never forget:

OVERALL RATING: ☆☆☆☆☆

Hungary

Draw the flag

ARRIVED | DEPARTED

Travel buddies:

Arrived by:

Highs F/C____ Lows F/C____

Currency:

Exchange: ____ = ____

HOW DO YOU SAY?

Language:

_____

Hello:

Goodbye:

Please:

Thank you:

Sights

☆☆☆☆☆
☆☆☆☆☆
☆☆☆☆☆
☆☆☆☆☆
☆☆☆☆☆

Cities

☆☆☆☆☆
☆☆☆☆☆
☆☆☆☆☆
☆☆☆☆☆
☆☆☆☆☆

I'll never forget:

_____
_____
_____
_____
_____
_____

OVERALL RATING: ☆☆☆☆☆

Iceland

Draw the flag

ARRIVED | DEPARTED

Travel buddies:

Arrived by:

Highs F/C____ Lows F/C____

Currency:

Exchange: ____ = ____

HOW DO YOU SAY?

Language:

_____

Hello:

Please:

Goodbye:

Thank you:

Sights

☆☆☆☆☆
☆☆☆☆☆
☆☆☆☆☆
☆☆☆☆☆
☆☆☆☆☆

Cities

☆☆☆☆☆
☆☆☆☆☆
☆☆☆☆☆
☆☆☆☆☆
☆☆☆☆☆

I'll never forget:

_____
_____
_____
_____

OVERALL RATING: ☆☆☆☆☆

Ireland

Draw the flag

ARRIVED | DEPARTED

Highs F/C_____ Lows F/C_____

Travel buddies:

Arrived by:

Currency:
Exchange: _____ = _____

HOW DO YOU SAY?

Language:
_____

Hello:

Goodbye:

Please:

Thank you:

Sights
☆☆☆☆☆
☆☆☆☆☆
☆☆☆☆☆
☆☆☆☆☆
☆☆☆☆☆

Cities
☆☆☆☆☆
☆☆☆☆☆
☆☆☆☆☆
☆☆☆☆☆
☆☆☆☆☆

I'll never forget:
_____
_____
_____
_____
_____
_____

OVERALL RATING: ☆☆☆☆☆

Italy

Draw the flag

ARRIVED | DEPARTED

Travel buddies:

Arrived by:

Highs F/C____ Lows F/C____

Currency:

Exchange: _____ = _____

HOW DO YOU SAY?

Language:

_____

Hello:

Goodbye:

Please:

Thank you:

Sights
☆☆☆☆☆
☆☆☆☆☆
☆☆☆☆☆
☆☆☆☆☆
☆☆☆☆☆

Cities
☆☆☆☆☆
☆☆☆☆☆
☆☆☆☆☆
☆☆☆☆☆
☆☆☆☆☆

I'll never forget:

_____

_____

_____

_____

_____

OVERALL RATING: ☆☆☆☆☆

Latvia

Draw the flag

ARRIVED | DEPARTED

Travel buddies:

Arrived by:

Highs F/C_____ Lows F/C_____

Currency:

Exchange: _____ = _____

HOW DO YOU SAY?

Language:

_____

Hello: Goodbye:

Please: Thank you:

Sights	
☆☆☆☆☆	
☆☆☆☆☆	
☆☆☆☆☆	
☆☆☆☆☆	
☆☆☆☆☆	

Cities	
☆☆☆☆☆	
☆☆☆☆☆	
☆☆☆☆☆	
☆☆☆☆☆	
☆☆☆☆☆	

I'll never forget:

_____

_____

_____

_____

_____

_____

OVERALL RATING: ☆☆☆☆☆

Liechtenstein

Draw the flag

ARRIVED   DEPARTED

Travel buddies:

Arrived by:

Highs F/C____ Lows F/C____

Currency:

Exchange: _____ = _____

HOW DO YOU SAY?

Language:

_____

Hello:

Please:

Goodbye:

Thank you:

Sights	Cities
☆☆☆☆☆	☆☆☆☆☆
☆☆☆☆☆	☆☆☆☆☆
☆☆☆☆☆	☆☆☆☆☆
☆☆☆☆☆	☆☆☆☆☆
☆☆☆☆☆	☆☆☆☆☆

I'll never forget:

_____

_____

_____

_____

_____

OVERALL RATING: ☆☆☆☆☆

Lithuania

Draw the flag

ARRIVED | DEPARTED

Highs F/C____ Lows F/C____

Travel buddies:

Arrived by:

Currency:

Exchange: ____ = ____

HOW DO YOU SAY?

Language:
_____

Hello:

Goodbye:

Please:

Thank you:

Sights
☆☆☆☆☆
☆☆☆☆☆
☆☆☆☆☆
☆☆☆☆☆
☆☆☆☆☆

Cities
☆☆☆☆☆
☆☆☆☆☆
☆☆☆☆☆
☆☆☆☆☆
☆☆☆☆☆

I'll never forget:

OVERALL RATING: ☆☆☆☆☆

Luxembourg

Draw the flag

ARRIVED | DEPARTED

Travel buddies:

Arrived by:

Highs F/C____ Lows F/C____

Currency:

Exchange: _____ = _____

HOW DO YOU SAY?

Language:
_____

Hello:

Goodbye:

Please:

Thank you:

Sights
☆☆☆☆☆
☆☆☆☆☆
☆☆☆☆☆
☆☆☆☆☆
☆☆☆☆☆

Cities
☆☆☆☆☆
☆☆☆☆☆
☆☆☆☆☆
☆☆☆☆☆
☆☆☆☆☆

I'll never forget:
_____
_____
_____
_____
_____

OVERALL RATING: ☆☆☆☆☆

Malta

Draw the flag

ARRIVED DEPARTED

Travel buddies:

Arrived by:

Highs F/C____ Lows F/C____

Currency:

Exchange: _____ = _____

HOW DO YOU SAY?

Language:

_____

Hello:

Goodbye:

Please:

Thank you:

Sights

☆☆☆☆☆
☆☆☆☆☆
☆☆☆☆☆
☆☆☆☆☆
☆☆☆☆☆

Cities

☆☆☆☆☆
☆☆☆☆☆
☆☆☆☆☆
☆☆☆☆☆
☆☆☆☆☆

I'll never forget:

_____
_____
_____
_____
_____
_____

OVERALL RATING: ☆☆☆☆☆

Moldova

Draw the flag

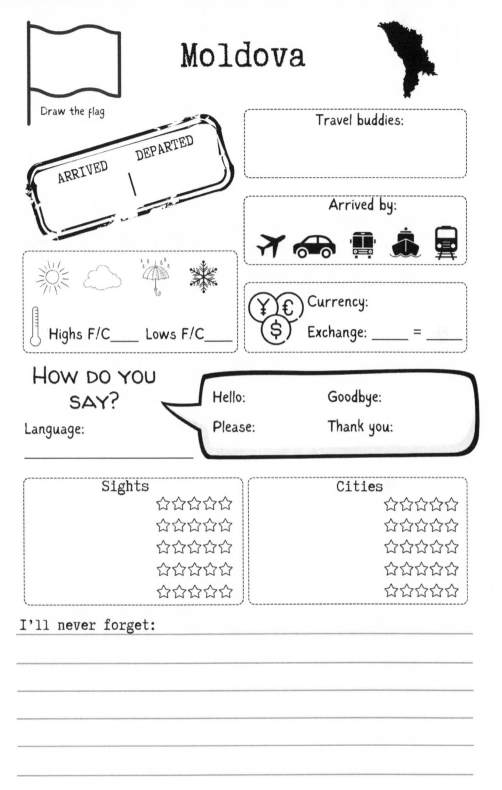

ARRIVED | DEPARTED

Travel buddies:

Arrived by:

Highs F/C____ Lows F/C____

Currency:

Exchange: _____ = _____

HOW DO YOU SAY?

Language:
_____

Hello:

Please:

Goodbye:

Thank you:

Sights
☆☆☆☆☆
☆☆☆☆☆
☆☆☆☆☆
☆☆☆☆☆
☆☆☆☆☆

Cities
☆☆☆☆☆
☆☆☆☆☆
☆☆☆☆☆
☆☆☆☆☆
☆☆☆☆☆

I'll never forget:
_____
_____
_____
_____
_____

OVERALL RATING: ☆☆☆☆☆

Monaco

Draw the flag

ARRIVED   DEPARTED

Travel buddies:

Arrived by:

Highs F/C____ Lows F/C____

Currency:

Exchange: _____ = _____

HOW DO YOU SAY?

Language:
_____

Hello:

Goodbye:

Please:

Thank you:

Sights	
☆☆☆☆☆	
☆☆☆☆☆	
☆☆☆☆☆	
☆☆☆☆☆	
☆☆☆☆☆	

Cities	
☆☆☆☆☆	
☆☆☆☆☆	
☆☆☆☆☆	
☆☆☆☆☆	
☆☆☆☆☆	

I'll never forget:

OVERALL RATING: ☆☆☆☆☆

Montenegro

Draw the flag

ARRIVED   DEPARTED

Highs F/C____   Lows F/C____

Travel buddies:

Arrived by:

Currency:

Exchange: _____ = ____

HOW DO YOU SAY?

Language:

_____

Hello: Goodbye:

Please: Thank you:

Sights		Cities	
☆☆☆☆☆		☆☆☆☆☆	
☆☆☆☆☆		☆☆☆☆☆	
☆☆☆☆☆		☆☆☆☆☆	
☆☆☆☆☆		☆☆☆☆☆	
☆☆☆☆☆		☆☆☆☆☆	

I'll never forget:

_____

_____

_____

_____

_____

OVERALL RATING: ☆☆☆☆☆

Netherlands

Draw the flag

ARRIVED | DEPARTED

Travel buddies:

Arrived by:

Highs F/C____ Lows F/C____

Currency:
Exchange: ____ = ____

HOW DO YOU SAY?

Language:
_____

Hello: Goodbye:

Please: Thank you:

Sights
☆☆☆☆☆
☆☆☆☆☆
☆☆☆☆☆
☆☆☆☆☆
☆☆☆☆☆

Cities
☆☆☆☆☆
☆☆☆☆☆
☆☆☆☆☆
☆☆☆☆☆
☆☆☆☆☆

I'll never forget:
_____
_____
_____
_____
_____
_____

OVERALL RATING: ☆☆☆☆☆

North Macedonia

Draw the flag

ARRIVED DEPARTED

Travel buddies:

Arrived by:

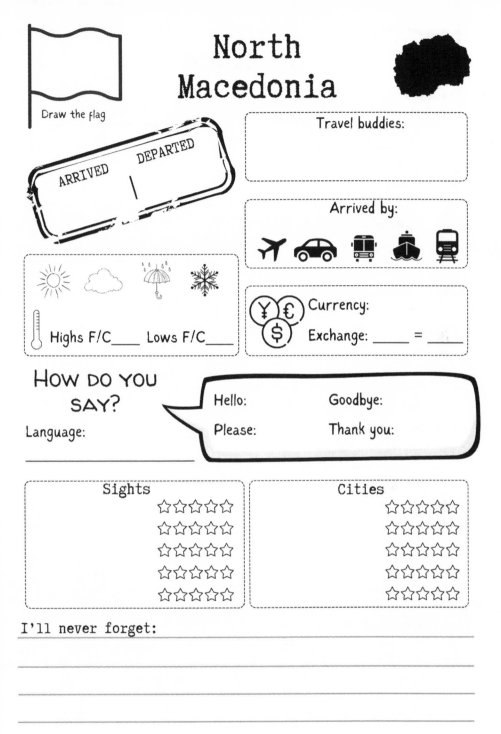

Highs F/C____ Lows F/C____

Currency:

Exchange: ____ = ____

HOW DO YOU SAY?

Language:

_____

Hello:

Please:

Goodbye:

Thank you:

Sights

☆☆☆☆☆
☆☆☆☆☆
☆☆☆☆☆
☆☆☆☆☆
☆☆☆☆☆

Cities

☆☆☆☆☆
☆☆☆☆☆
☆☆☆☆☆
☆☆☆☆☆
☆☆☆☆☆

I'll never forget:

_____
_____
_____
_____
_____

OVERALL RATING: ☆☆☆☆☆

Norway

Draw the flag

ARRIVED | DEPARTED

Highs F/C____ Lows F/C____

Travel buddies:

Arrived by:

Currency:

Exchange: _____ = _____

HOW DO YOU SAY?

Language:

_____

Hello:

Goodbye:

Please:

Thank you:

Sights	Cities
☆☆☆☆☆	☆☆☆☆☆
☆☆☆☆☆	☆☆☆☆☆
☆☆☆☆☆	☆☆☆☆☆
☆☆☆☆☆	☆☆☆☆☆
☆☆☆☆☆	☆☆☆☆☆

I'll never forget:

_____

_____

_____

_____

_____

_____

OVERALL RATING: ☆☆☆☆☆

Poland

Draw the flag

ARRIVED | DEPARTED

Travel buddies:

Arrived by:

Highs F/C_____ Lows F/C_____

Currency:

Exchange: _____ = _____

How do you say?

Language:
_____

Hello:

Goodbye:

Please:

Thank you:

Sights

⭐⭐⭐⭐⭐
⭐⭐⭐⭐⭐
⭐⭐⭐⭐⭐
⭐⭐⭐⭐⭐
⭐⭐⭐⭐⭐

Cities

⭐⭐⭐⭐⭐
⭐⭐⭐⭐⭐
⭐⭐⭐⭐⭐
⭐⭐⭐⭐⭐
⭐⭐⭐⭐⭐

I'll never forget:

OVERALL RATING: ⭐⭐⭐⭐⭐

Portugal

Draw the flag

ARRIVED | DEPARTED

Travel buddies:

Arrived by:

Highs F/C____ Lows F/C____

Currency:

Exchange: ____ = ____

HOW DO YOU SAY?

Language:

_____

Hello:

Please:

Goodbye:

Thank you:

Sights

☆☆☆☆☆
☆☆☆☆☆
☆☆☆☆☆
☆☆☆☆☆
☆☆☆☆☆

Cities

☆☆☆☆☆
☆☆☆☆☆
☆☆☆☆☆
☆☆☆☆☆
☆☆☆☆☆

I'll never forget:

OVERALL RATING: ☆☆☆☆☆

Romania

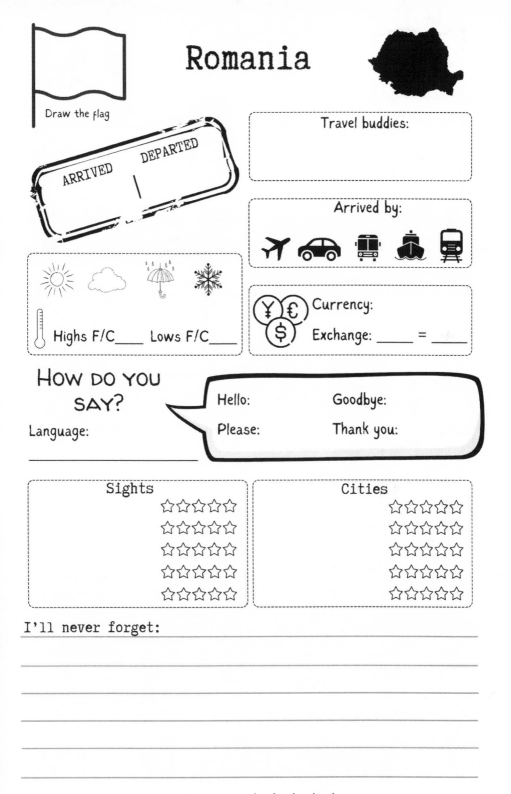

Draw the flag

ARRIVED   DEPARTED

Travel buddies:

Arrived by:

Highs F/C____ Lows F/C____

Currency:

Exchange: _____ = _____

HOW DO YOU SAY?

Language:
_____

Hello:

Goodbye:

Please:

Thank you:

Sights
☆☆☆☆☆
☆☆☆☆☆
☆☆☆☆☆
☆☆☆☆☆
☆☆☆☆☆

Cities
☆☆☆☆☆
☆☆☆☆☆
☆☆☆☆☆
☆☆☆☆☆
☆☆☆☆☆

I'll never forget:
_____
_____
_____
_____
_____

OVERALL RATING: ☆☆☆☆☆

Russia

Draw the flag

ARRIVED | DEPARTED

Travel buddies:

Arrived by:

Highs F/C____ Lows F/C____

Currency:

Exchange: _____ = _____

HOW DO YOU SAY?

Language:
_____

Hello:

Goodbye:

Please:

Thank you:

Sights		Cities	
☆☆☆☆☆		☆☆☆☆☆	
☆☆☆☆☆		☆☆☆☆☆	
☆☆☆☆☆		☆☆☆☆☆	
☆☆☆☆☆		☆☆☆☆☆	
☆☆☆☆☆		☆☆☆☆☆	

I'll never forget:
_____
_____
_____
_____
_____
_____

OVERALL RATING: ☆☆☆☆☆

San Marino

Draw the flag

ARRIVED | DEPARTED

Travel buddies:

Arrived by:

Highs F/C____ Lows F/C____

Currency:

Exchange: _____ = _____

HOW DO YOU SAY?

Language:

_____

Hello:

Please:

Goodbye:

Thank you:

Sights	Cities
☆☆☆☆☆	☆☆☆☆☆
☆☆☆☆☆	☆☆☆☆☆
☆☆☆☆☆	☆☆☆☆☆
☆☆☆☆☆	☆☆☆☆☆
☆☆☆☆☆	☆☆☆☆☆

I'll never forget:

_____

_____

_____

_____

_____

OVERALL RATING: ☆☆☆☆☆

Serbia

Draw the flag

ARRIVED DEPARTED

Travel buddies:

Arrived by:

Highs F/C____ Lows F/C____

Currency:
Exchange: ____ = ____

HOW DO YOU SAY?

Language:
_____

Hello: Goodbye:

Please: Thank you:

Sights
☆☆☆☆☆
☆☆☆☆☆
☆☆☆☆☆
☆☆☆☆☆
☆☆☆☆☆

Cities
☆☆☆☆☆
☆☆☆☆☆
☆☆☆☆☆
☆☆☆☆☆
☆☆☆☆☆

I'll never forget:

OVERALL RATING: ☆☆☆☆☆

Slovakia

Draw the flag

ARRIVED   DEPARTED

Travel buddies:

Arrived by:

Highs F/C____ Lows F/C____

Currency:

Exchange: _____ = _____

HOW DO YOU SAY?

Language:
_____

Hello:

Goodbye:

Please:

Thank you:

Sights

☆☆☆☆☆
☆☆☆☆☆
☆☆☆☆☆
☆☆☆☆☆
☆☆☆☆☆

Cities

☆☆☆☆☆
☆☆☆☆☆
☆☆☆☆☆
☆☆☆☆☆
☆☆☆☆☆

I'll never forget:

_____
_____
_____
_____
_____

OVERALL RATING: ☆☆☆☆☆

Slovenia

Draw the flag

ARRIVED | DEPARTED

Highs F/C____ Lows F/C____

Travel buddies:

Arrived by:

Currency:

Exchange: _____ = _____

HOW DO YOU SAY?

Language:

_____

Hello:

Goodbye:

Please:

Thank you:

Sights

☆☆☆☆☆
☆☆☆☆☆
☆☆☆☆☆
☆☆☆☆☆
☆☆☆☆☆

Cities

☆☆☆☆☆
☆☆☆☆☆
☆☆☆☆☆
☆☆☆☆☆
☆☆☆☆☆

I'll never forget:

_____
_____
_____
_____
_____
_____

OVERALL RATING: ☆☆☆☆☆

Spain

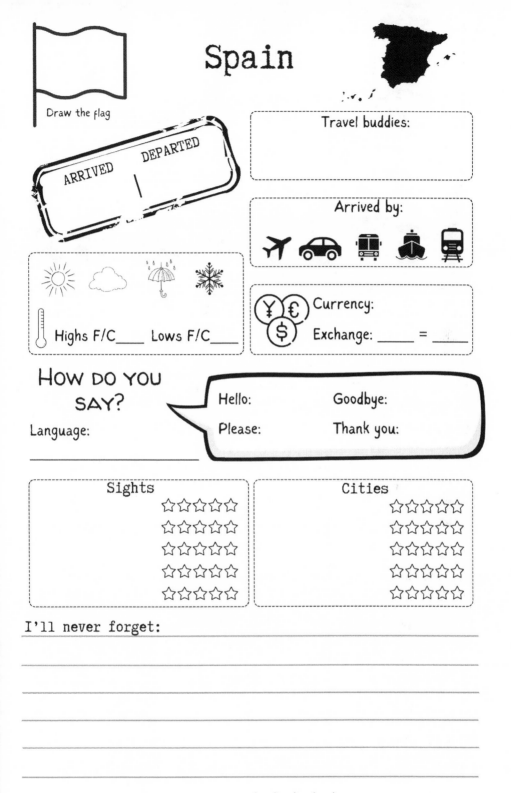

Draw the flag

ARRIVED | DEPARTED

Highs F/C____ Lows F/C____

Travel buddies:

Arrived by:

Currency:
Exchange: _____ = _____

HOW DO YOU SAY?

Language:
_____

Hello:

Goodbye:

Please:

Thank you:

Sights ☆☆☆☆☆ ☆☆☆☆☆ ☆☆☆☆☆ ☆☆☆☆☆ ☆☆☆☆☆

Cities ☆☆☆☆☆ ☆☆☆☆☆ ☆☆☆☆☆ ☆☆☆☆☆ ☆☆☆☆☆

I'll never forget:

OVERALL RATING: ☆☆☆☆☆

Sweden

Draw the flag

ARRIVED | DEPARTED

Travel buddies:

Arrived by:

Highs F/C____ Lows F/C____

Currency:

Exchange: ____ = ____

HOW DO YOU SAY?

Language:

_____

Hello:

Goodbye:

Please:

Thank you:

Sights
☆☆☆☆☆
☆☆☆☆☆
☆☆☆☆☆
☆☆☆☆☆
☆☆☆☆☆

Cities
☆☆☆☆☆
☆☆☆☆☆
☆☆☆☆☆
☆☆☆☆☆
☆☆☆☆☆

I'll never forget:

_____
_____
_____
_____
_____
_____

OVERALL RATING: ☆☆☆☆☆

Switzerland

Draw the flag

ARRIVED | DEPARTED

Travel buddies:

Arrived by:

Highs F/C____ Lows F/C____

Currency:

Exchange: ____ = ____

HOW DO YOU SAY?

Language:

_____

Hello:

Please:

Goodbye:

Thank you:

Sights	Cities
☆☆☆☆☆	☆☆☆☆☆
☆☆☆☆☆	☆☆☆☆☆
☆☆☆☆☆	☆☆☆☆☆
☆☆☆☆☆	☆☆☆☆☆
☆☆☆☆☆	☆☆☆☆☆

I'll never forget:

_____

_____

_____

_____

_____

OVERALL RATING: ☆☆☆☆☆

Ukraine

Draw the flag

ARRIVED | DEPARTED

Highs F/C____ Lows F/C____

Travel buddies:

Arrived by:

Currency:
Exchange: ____ = ____

HOW DO YOU SAY?

Language:
_____

Hello:

Goodbye:

Please:

Thank you:

Sights
☆☆☆☆☆
☆☆☆☆☆
☆☆☆☆☆
☆☆☆☆☆
☆☆☆☆☆

Cities
☆☆☆☆☆
☆☆☆☆☆
☆☆☆☆☆
☆☆☆☆☆
☆☆☆☆☆

I'll never forget:
_____
_____
_____
_____
_____
_____

OVERALL RATING: ☆☆☆☆☆

United Kingdom

Draw the flag

ARRIVED   DEPARTED

Highs F/C____ Lows F/C____

Travel buddies:

Arrived by:

Currency:

Exchange: _____ = _____

HOW DO YOU SAY?

Language:

_____

Hello: Goodbye:

Please: Thank you:

Sights	Cities
☆☆☆☆☆	☆☆☆☆☆
☆☆☆☆☆	☆☆☆☆☆
☆☆☆☆☆	☆☆☆☆☆
☆☆☆☆☆	☆☆☆☆☆
☆☆☆☆☆	☆☆☆☆☆

I'll never forget:

_____

_____

_____

_____

_____

OVERALL RATING: ☆☆☆☆☆

Vatican City

Draw the flag

ARRIVED | DEPARTED

Highs F/C____ Lows F/C____

Travel buddies:

Arrived by:

Currency:

Exchange: ____ = ____

HOW DO YOU SAY?

Language:
_____

Hello:

Goodbye:

Please:

Thank you:

Sights

☆☆☆☆☆
☆☆☆☆☆
☆☆☆☆☆
☆☆☆☆☆
☆☆☆☆☆

Cities

☆☆☆☆☆
☆☆☆☆☆
☆☆☆☆☆
☆☆☆☆☆
☆☆☆☆☆

I'll never forget:

OVERALL RATING: ☆☆☆☆☆

Draw the flag

Special territory/Other

ARRIVED | DEPARTED

Travel buddies:

Arrived by:

Highs F/C____ Lows F/C____

Currency:

Exchange: _____ = _____

HOW DO YOU SAY?

Language:
_____

Hello:

Goodbye:

Please:

Thank you:

Sights

☆☆☆☆☆
☆☆☆☆☆
☆☆☆☆☆
☆☆☆☆☆
☆☆☆☆☆

Cities

☆☆☆☆☆
☆☆☆☆☆
☆☆☆☆☆
☆☆☆☆☆
☆☆☆☆☆

I'll never forget:

OVERALL RATING: ☆☆☆☆☆

North America

Travel is fatal to prejudice, bigotry, and narrow-mindedness, and many people need it sorely on these accounts.

—Mark Twain

Antigua and Barbuda

Draw the flag

ARRIVED | DEPARTED

Travel buddies:

Arrived by:

Highs F/C____ Lows F/C____

Currency:

Exchange: _____ = _____

HOW DO YOU SAY?

Language:
_____

Hello:

Goodbye:

Please:

Thank you:

Sights

☆☆☆☆☆
☆☆☆☆☆
☆☆☆☆☆
☆☆☆☆☆
☆☆☆☆☆

Cities

☆☆☆☆☆
☆☆☆☆☆
☆☆☆☆☆
☆☆☆☆☆
☆☆☆☆☆

I'll never forget:

_____
_____
_____
_____
_____

OVERALL RATING: ☆☆☆☆☆

The Bahamas

Draw the flag

ARRIVED   DEPARTED

Travel buddies:

Arrived by:

Highs F/C____   Lows F/C____

Currency:
Exchange: _____ = _____

HOW DO YOU SAY?

Language:
_____

Hello:

Goodbye:

Please:

Thank you:

Sights
☆☆☆☆☆
☆☆☆☆☆
☆☆☆☆☆
☆☆☆☆☆
☆☆☆☆☆

Cities
☆☆☆☆☆
☆☆☆☆☆
☆☆☆☆☆
☆☆☆☆☆
☆☆☆☆☆

I'll never forget:
_____
_____
_____
_____
_____
_____

OVERALL RATING: ☆☆☆☆☆

Barbados

Draw the flag

ARRIVED | DEPARTED

Travel buddies:

Arrived by:

Currency:
Exchange: _____ = _____

Highs F/C____ Lows F/C____

HOW DO YOU SAY?

Language:
_____

Hello:

Goodbye:

Please:

Thank you:

Sights	Cities
☆☆☆☆☆	☆☆☆☆☆
☆☆☆☆☆	☆☆☆☆☆
☆☆☆☆☆	☆☆☆☆☆
☆☆☆☆☆	☆☆☆☆☆
☆☆☆☆☆	☆☆☆☆☆

I'll never forget:

_____

_____

_____

_____

_____

OVERALL RATING: ☆☆☆☆☆

Belize

Draw the flag

ARRIVED | DEPARTED

Highs F/C____ Lows F/C____

Travel buddies:

Arrived by:

Currency:

Exchange: ____ = ____

HOW DO YOU SAY?

Language:
_____

Hello:

Goodbye:

Please:

Thank you:

Sights

☆☆☆☆☆
☆☆☆☆☆
☆☆☆☆☆
☆☆☆☆☆
☆☆☆☆☆

Cities

☆☆☆☆☆
☆☆☆☆☆
☆☆☆☆☆
☆☆☆☆☆
☆☆☆☆☆

I'll never forget:

_____
_____
_____
_____
_____
_____

OVERALL RATING: ☆☆☆☆☆

Canada

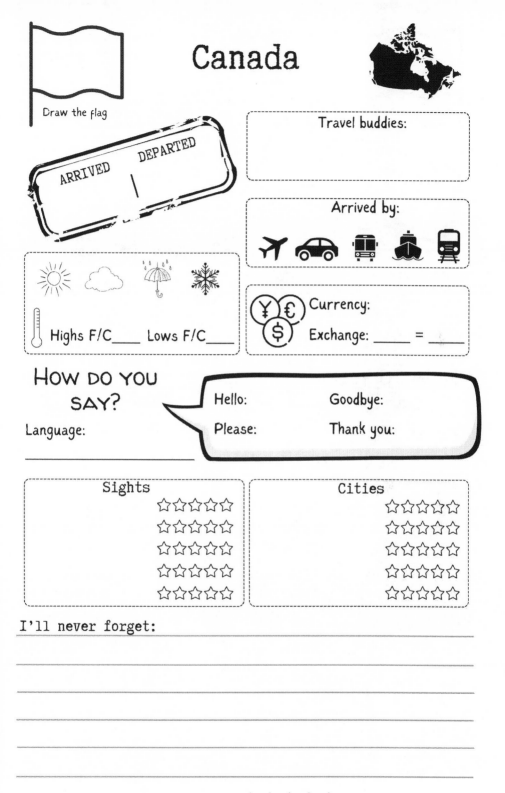

Draw the flag

ARRIVED DEPARTED

Highs F/C____ Lows F/C____

Travel buddies:

Arrived by:

Currency:
Exchange: _____ = _____

HOW DO YOU SAY?

Language:
_____

Hello: Goodbye:

Please: Thank you:

Sights
☆☆☆☆☆
☆☆☆☆☆
☆☆☆☆☆
☆☆☆☆☆
☆☆☆☆☆

Cities
☆☆☆☆☆
☆☆☆☆☆
☆☆☆☆☆
☆☆☆☆☆
☆☆☆☆☆

I'll never forget:

OVERALL RATING: ☆☆☆☆☆

Costa Rica

Draw the flag

ARRIVED | DEPARTED

Highs F/C____ Lows F/C____

Travel buddies:

Arrived by:

Currency:

Exchange: ____ = ____

HOW DO YOU SAY?

Language:
_____

Hello: Goodbye:

Please: Thank you:

Sights
☆☆☆☆☆
☆☆☆☆☆
☆☆☆☆☆
☆☆☆☆☆
☆☆☆☆☆

Cities
☆☆☆☆☆
☆☆☆☆☆
☆☆☆☆☆
☆☆☆☆☆
☆☆☆☆☆

I'll never forget:
_____
_____
_____
_____
_____

OVERALL RATING: ☆☆☆☆☆

Dominica

Draw the flag

ARRIVED | DEPARTED

Travel buddies:

Arrived by:
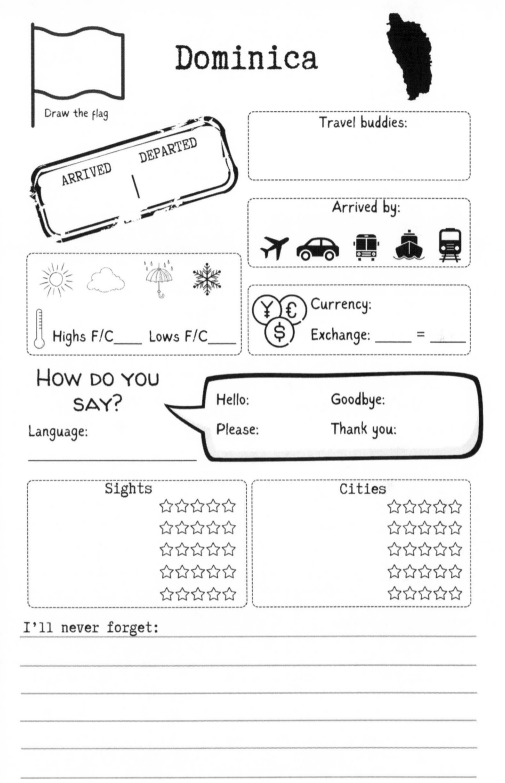

Highs F/C____ Lows F/C____

Currency:
Exchange: ____ = ____

HOW DO YOU SAY?

Language:
_____

Hello:

Goodbye:

Please:

Thank you:

Sights
☆☆☆☆☆
☆☆☆☆☆
☆☆☆☆☆
☆☆☆☆☆
☆☆☆☆☆

Cities
☆☆☆☆☆
☆☆☆☆☆
☆☆☆☆☆
☆☆☆☆☆
☆☆☆☆☆

I'll never forget:

OVERALL RATING: ☆☆☆☆☆

Dominican Republic

Draw the flag

ARRIVED | DEPARTED

Travel buddies:

Arrived by:

Highs F/C____ Lows F/C____

Currency:

Exchange: ____ = ____

HOW DO YOU SAY?

Language:
_____

Hello:

Please:

Goodbye:

Thank you:

Sights

☆☆☆☆☆
☆☆☆☆☆
☆☆☆☆☆
☆☆☆☆☆
☆☆☆☆☆

Cities

☆☆☆☆☆
☆☆☆☆☆
☆☆☆☆☆
☆☆☆☆☆
☆☆☆☆☆

I'll never forget:
_____
_____
_____
_____
_____
_____

OVERALL RATING: ☆☆☆☆☆

El Salvador

Draw the flag

ARRIVED | DEPARTED

Travel buddies:

Arrived by:

Highs F/C____ Lows F/C____

Currency:

Exchange: _____ = _____

HOW DO YOU SAY?

Language:

_____

Hello:

Please:

Goodbye:

Thank you:

Sights

☆☆☆☆☆
☆☆☆☆☆
☆☆☆☆☆
☆☆☆☆☆
☆☆☆☆☆

Cities

☆☆☆☆☆
☆☆☆☆☆
☆☆☆☆☆
☆☆☆☆☆
☆☆☆☆☆

I'll never forget:

_____

_____

_____

_____

_____

OVERALL RATING: ☆☆☆☆☆

Grenada

Draw the flag

ARRIVED | DEPARTED

Highs F/C____ Lows F/C____

Travel buddies:

Arrived by:

Currency:
Exchange: ____ = ____

HOW DO YOU SAY?

Language:
_____

Hello:

Goodbye:

Please:

Thank you:

Sights		Cities	
☆☆☆☆☆		☆☆☆☆☆	
☆☆☆☆☆		☆☆☆☆☆	
☆☆☆☆☆		☆☆☆☆☆	
☆☆☆☆☆		☆☆☆☆☆	
☆☆☆☆☆		☆☆☆☆☆	

I'll never forget:

_____
_____
_____
_____
_____
_____

OVERALL RATING: ☆☆☆☆☆

Guatemala

Draw the flag

ARRIVED   DEPARTED

Highs F/C____   Lows F/C____

Travel buddies:

Arrived by:

Currency:

Exchange: _____ = _____

HOW DO YOU SAY?

Language:

_____

Hello: Goodbye:

Please: Thank you:

Sights	Cities
☆☆☆☆☆	☆☆☆☆☆
☆☆☆☆☆	☆☆☆☆☆
☆☆☆☆☆	☆☆☆☆☆
☆☆☆☆☆	☆☆☆☆☆
☆☆☆☆☆	☆☆☆☆☆

I'll never forget:

_____

_____

_____

_____

_____

OVERALL RATING: ☆☆☆☆☆

Haiti

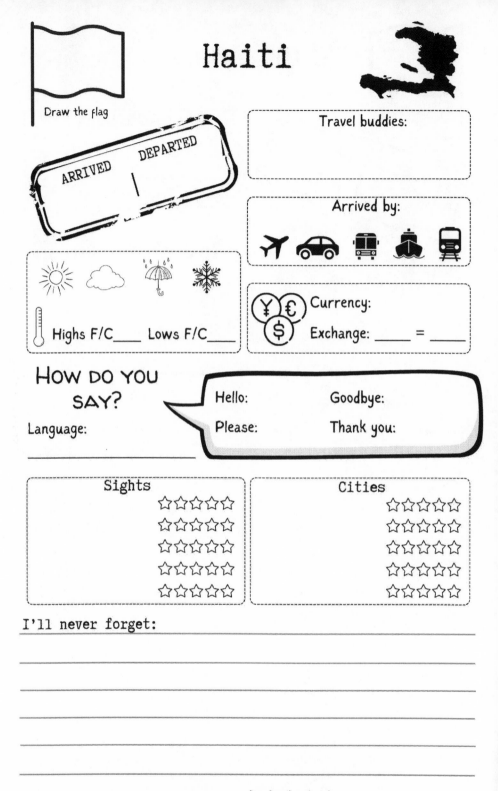

Draw the flag

ARRIVED   DEPARTED

Travel buddies:

Arrived by:

Highs F/C____   Lows F/C____

Currency:

Exchange: _____ = _____

HOW DO YOU SAY?

Language:

_____

Hello: Goodbye:

Please: Thank you:

Sights

☆☆☆☆☆
☆☆☆☆☆
☆☆☆☆☆
☆☆☆☆☆
☆☆☆☆☆

Cities

☆☆☆☆☆
☆☆☆☆☆
☆☆☆☆☆
☆☆☆☆☆
☆☆☆☆☆

I'll never forget:

OVERALL RATING: ☆☆☆☆☆

Honduras

Draw the flag

ARRIVED | DEPARTED

Travel buddies:

Arrived by:
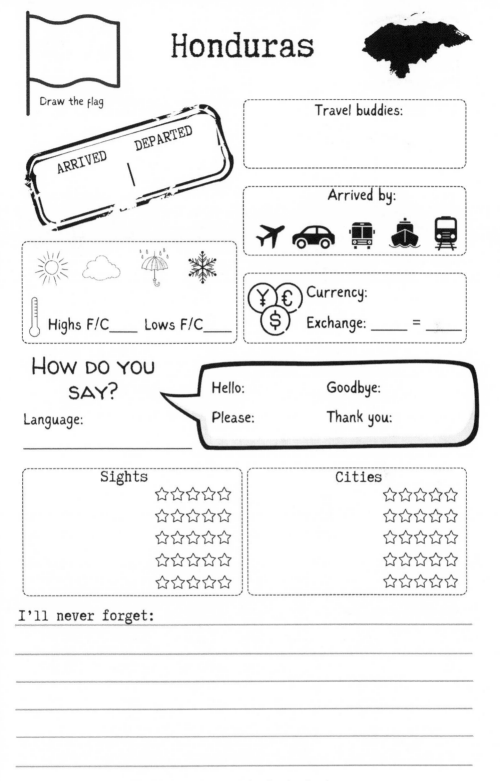

Highs F/C____ Lows F/C____

Currency:
Exchange: ____ = ____

HOW DO YOU SAY?

Language:
_____

Hello: Goodbye:

Please: Thank you:

Sights
☆☆☆☆☆
☆☆☆☆☆
☆☆☆☆☆
☆☆☆☆☆
☆☆☆☆☆

Cities
☆☆☆☆☆
☆☆☆☆☆
☆☆☆☆☆
☆☆☆☆☆
☆☆☆☆☆

I'll never forget:
_____
_____
_____
_____
_____

OVERALL RATING: ☆☆☆☆☆

Jamaica

Draw the flag

ARRIVED | DEPARTED

Highs F/C____ Lows F/C____

Travel buddies:

Arrived by:

Currency:

Exchange: ____ = ____

HOW DO YOU SAY?

Language:
_____

Hello:

Goodbye:

Please:

Thank you:

Sights

☆☆☆☆☆
☆☆☆☆☆
☆☆☆☆☆
☆☆☆☆☆
☆☆☆☆☆

Cities

☆☆☆☆☆
☆☆☆☆☆
☆☆☆☆☆
☆☆☆☆☆
☆☆☆☆☆

I'll never forget:

_____
_____
_____
_____
_____
_____

OVERALL RATING: ☆☆☆☆☆

Mexico

Draw the flag

ARRIVED · DEPARTED

Travel buddies:

Arrived by:

Highs F/C____ Lows F/C____

Currency:

Exchange: ____ = ____

HOW DO YOU SAY?

Language:

_____

Hello:

Please:

Goodbye:

Thank you:

Sights		Cities	
☆☆☆☆☆		☆☆☆☆☆	
☆☆☆☆☆		☆☆☆☆☆	
☆☆☆☆☆		☆☆☆☆☆	
☆☆☆☆☆		☆☆☆☆☆	
☆☆☆☆☆		☆☆☆☆☆	

I'll never forget:

_____

_____

_____

_____

_____

OVERALL RATING: ☆☆☆☆☆

Nicaragua

Draw the flag

ARRIVED | DEPARTED

Highs F/C____ Lows F/C____

Travel buddies:

Arrived by:

Currency:

Exchange: _____ = _____

HOW DO YOU SAY?

Language:
_____

Hello:

Goodbye:

Please:

Thank you:

Sights

☆☆☆☆☆
☆☆☆☆☆
☆☆☆☆☆
☆☆☆☆☆
☆☆☆☆☆

Cities

☆☆☆☆☆
☆☆☆☆☆
☆☆☆☆☆
☆☆☆☆☆
☆☆☆☆☆

I'll never forget:

_____
_____
_____
_____
_____

OVERALL RATING: ☆☆☆☆☆

Panama

Draw the flag

ARRIVED | DEPARTED

Travel buddies:

Arrived by:

Highs F/C____ Lows F/C____

Currency:

Exchange: _____ = _____

HOW DO YOU SAY?

Language:

_____

Hello:

Please:

Goodbye:

Thank you:

Sights
☆☆☆☆☆
☆☆☆☆☆
☆☆☆☆☆
☆☆☆☆☆
☆☆☆☆☆

Cities
☆☆☆☆☆
☆☆☆☆☆
☆☆☆☆☆
☆☆☆☆☆
☆☆☆☆☆

I'll never forget:

_____
_____
_____
_____
_____

OVERALL RATING: ☆☆☆☆☆

Saint Kitts and Nevis

Draw the flag

ARRIVED   DEPARTED

Travel buddies:

Arrived by:

Highs F/C____ Lows F/C____

Currency:

Exchange: _____ = _____

HOW DO YOU SAY?

Language:
_____

Hello: Goodbye:

Please: Thank you:

Sights
☆☆☆☆☆
☆☆☆☆☆
☆☆☆☆☆
☆☆☆☆☆
☆☆☆☆☆

Cities
☆☆☆☆☆
☆☆☆☆☆
☆☆☆☆☆
☆☆☆☆☆
☆☆☆☆☆

I'll never forget:

_____
_____
_____
_____
_____

OVERALL RATING: ☆☆☆☆☆

Saint Lucia

Draw the flag

ARRIVED   DEPARTED

Travel buddies:

Arrived by:

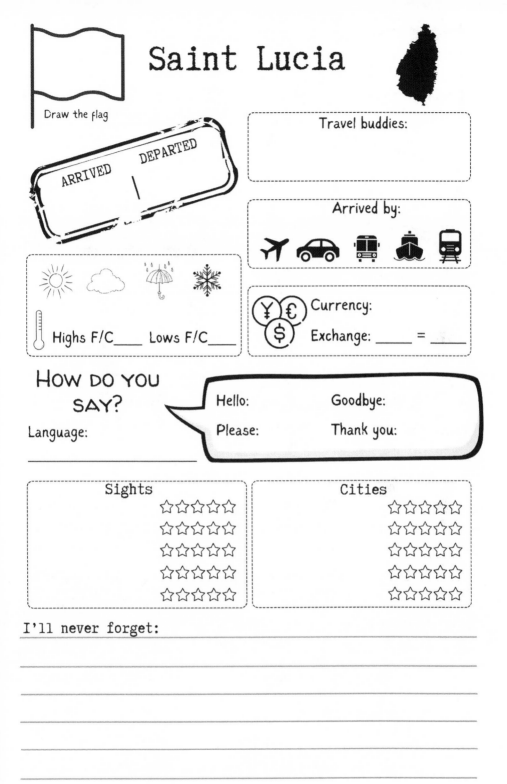

Highs F/C____ Lows F/C____

Currency:

Exchange: _____ = _____

HOW DO YOU SAY?

Language:
_____

Hello: Goodbye:

Please: Thank you:

Sights
☆☆☆☆☆
☆☆☆☆☆
☆☆☆☆☆
☆☆☆☆☆
☆☆☆☆☆

Cities
☆☆☆☆☆
☆☆☆☆☆
☆☆☆☆☆
☆☆☆☆☆
☆☆☆☆☆

I'll never forget:
_____
_____
_____
_____
_____

OVERALL RATING: ☆☆☆☆☆

Saint Vincent and the Grenadines

Draw the flag

ARRIVED | DEPARTED

Travel buddies:

Arrived by:

Highs F/C____ Lows F/C____

Currency:

Exchange: ____ = ____

HOW DO YOU SAY?

Language:
_____

Hello:

Goodbye:

Please:

Thank you:

Sights		Cities	
☆☆☆☆☆		☆☆☆☆☆	
☆☆☆☆☆		☆☆☆☆☆	
☆☆☆☆☆		☆☆☆☆☆	
☆☆☆☆☆		☆☆☆☆☆	
☆☆☆☆☆		☆☆☆☆☆	

I'll never forget:

_____
_____
_____
_____
_____

OVERALL RATING: ☆☆☆☆☆

Trinidad and Tobago

Draw the flag

ARRIVED | DEPARTED

Travel buddies:

Arrived by:

Highs F/C____ Lows F/C____

Currency:

Exchange: ____ = ____

HOW DO YOU SAY?

Language:

_____

Hello:

Please:

Goodbye:

Thank you:

Sights

☆☆☆☆☆
☆☆☆☆☆
☆☆☆☆☆
☆☆☆☆☆
☆☆☆☆☆

Cities

☆☆☆☆☆
☆☆☆☆☆
☆☆☆☆☆
☆☆☆☆☆
☆☆☆☆☆

I'll never forget:

OVERALL RATING: ☆☆☆☆☆

United States of America

Draw the flag

ARRIVED   DEPARTED

Highs F/C____ Lows F/C____

Travel buddies:

Arrived by:

Currency:
Exchange: ____ = ____

HOW DO YOU SAY?

Language:
_____

Hello: Goodbye:

Please: Thank you:

Sights				
☆	☆	☆	☆	☆
☆	☆	☆	☆	☆
☆	☆	☆	☆	☆
☆	☆	☆	☆	☆
☆	☆	☆	☆	☆

Cities				
☆	☆	☆	☆	☆
☆	☆	☆	☆	☆
☆	☆	☆	☆	☆
☆	☆	☆	☆	☆
☆	☆	☆	☆	☆

I'll never forget:

OVERALL RATING: ☆☆☆☆☆

Draw the flag

Special territory/Other

ARRIVED   DEPARTED

Travel buddies:

Arrived by:

Highs F/C____   Lows F/C____

Currency:

Exchange: _____ = _____

HOW DO YOU
SAY?

Language:

Hello: Goodbye:

Please: Thank you:

Sights
☆☆☆☆☆
☆☆☆☆☆
☆☆☆☆☆
☆☆☆☆☆
☆☆☆☆☆

Cities
☆☆☆☆☆
☆☆☆☆☆
☆☆☆☆☆
☆☆☆☆☆
☆☆☆☆☆

I'll never forget:

OVERALL RATING: ☆☆☆☆☆

South America

Travel is never a matter of money but
of courage.

—Paulo Coelho

Argentina

Draw the flag

ARRIVED | DEPARTED

Travel buddies:

Arrived by:

Highs F/C____ Lows F/C____

Currency:

Exchange: _____ = _____

HOW DO YOU SAY?

Language:
_____

Hello:

Goodbye:

Please:

Thank you:

Sights
☆☆☆☆☆
☆☆☆☆☆
☆☆☆☆☆
☆☆☆☆☆
☆☆☆☆☆

Cities
☆☆☆☆☆
☆☆☆☆☆
☆☆☆☆☆
☆☆☆☆☆
☆☆☆☆☆

I'll never forget:
_____
_____
_____
_____
_____

OVERALL RATING: ☆☆☆☆☆

Bolivia

Draw the flag

ARRIVED | DEPARTED

Highs F/C____ Lows F/C____

Travel buddies:

Arrived by:

Currency:

Exchange: ____ = ____

HOW DO YOU SAY?

Language:

_____

Hello:

Goodbye:

Please:

Thank you:

Sights

☆☆☆☆☆
☆☆☆☆☆
☆☆☆☆☆
☆☆☆☆☆
☆☆☆☆☆

Cities

☆☆☆☆☆
☆☆☆☆☆
☆☆☆☆☆
☆☆☆☆☆
☆☆☆☆☆

I'll never forget:

_____
_____
_____
_____
_____
_____

OVERALL RATING: ☆☆☆☆☆

Brazil

Draw the flag

ARRIVED   DEPARTED

Travel buddies:

Arrived by:

Highs F/C____ Lows F/C____

Currency:

Exchange: _____ = _____

HOW DO YOU SAY?

Language:
_____

Hello:

Goodbye:

Please:

Thank you:

Sights
☆☆☆☆☆
☆☆☆☆☆
☆☆☆☆☆
☆☆☆☆☆
☆☆☆☆☆

Cities
☆☆☆☆☆
☆☆☆☆☆
☆☆☆☆☆
☆☆☆☆☆
☆☆☆☆☆

I'll never forget:
_____
_____
_____
_____
_____

OVERALL RATING: ☆☆☆☆☆

Chile

Draw the flag

ARRIVED | DEPARTED

Highs F/C___ Lows F/C___

Travel buddies:

Arrived by:

Currency:

Exchange: ___ = ___

HOW DO YOU SAY?

Language:
_____

Hello:

Goodbye:

Please:

Thank you:

Sights
☆☆☆☆☆
☆☆☆☆☆
☆☆☆☆☆
☆☆☆☆☆
☆☆☆☆☆

Cities
☆☆☆☆☆
☆☆☆☆☆
☆☆☆☆☆
☆☆☆☆☆
☆☆☆☆☆

I'll never forget:
_____
_____
_____
_____
_____
_____

OVERALL RATING: ☆☆☆☆☆

Colombia

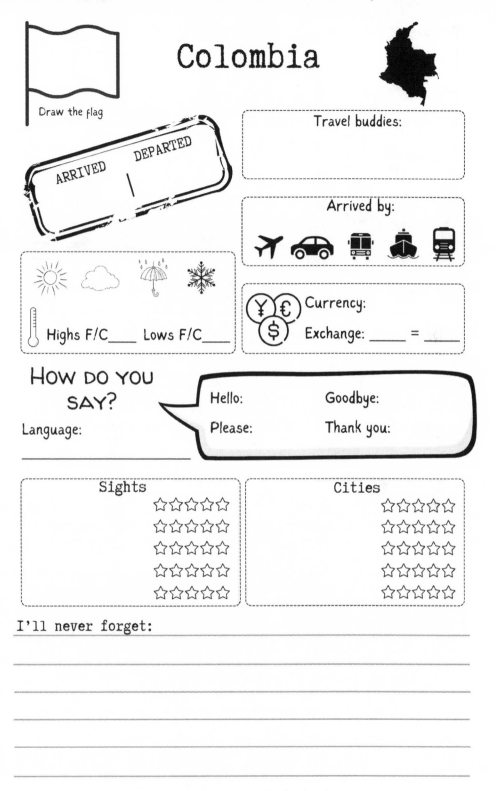

Draw the flag

ARRIVED DEPARTED

Highs F/C____ Lows F/C____

Travel buddies:

Arrived by:

Currency:

Exchange: _____ = _____

HOW DO YOU SAY?

Language:

_____

Hello: Goodbye:

Please: Thank you:

Sights
☆☆☆☆☆
☆☆☆☆☆
☆☆☆☆☆
☆☆☆☆☆
☆☆☆☆☆

Cities
☆☆☆☆☆
☆☆☆☆☆
☆☆☆☆☆
☆☆☆☆☆
☆☆☆☆☆

I'll never forget:

_____

_____

_____

_____

_____

OVERALL RATING: ☆☆☆☆☆

Ecuador

Draw the flag

ARRIVED   DEPARTED

Travel buddies:

Arrived by:

Highs F/C____ Lows F/C____

Currency:
Exchange: _____ = _____

HOW DO YOU SAY?

Language:
_____

Hello:

Goodbye:

Please:

Thank you:

Sights
☆☆☆☆☆
☆☆☆☆☆
☆☆☆☆☆
☆☆☆☆☆
☆☆☆☆☆

Cities
☆☆☆☆☆
☆☆☆☆☆
☆☆☆☆☆
☆☆☆☆☆
☆☆☆☆☆

I'll never forget:

OVERALL RATING: ☆☆☆☆☆

Guyana

Draw the flag

ARRIVED   DEPARTED

Travel buddies:

Arrived by:

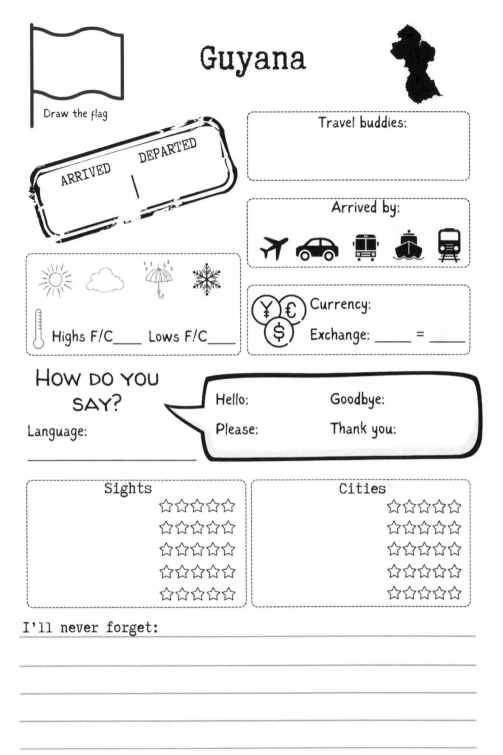

Highs F/C____ Lows F/C____

Currency:

Exchange: ____ = ____

HOW DO YOU SAY?

Language:
_____

Hello: Goodbye:

Please: Thank you:

Sights
☆☆☆☆☆
☆☆☆☆☆
☆☆☆☆☆
☆☆☆☆☆
☆☆☆☆☆

Cities
☆☆☆☆☆
☆☆☆☆☆
☆☆☆☆☆
☆☆☆☆☆
☆☆☆☆☆

I'll never forget:
_____
_____
_____
_____
_____

OVERALL RATING: ☆☆☆☆☆

Paraguay

Draw the flag

ARRIVED | DEPARTED

Travel buddies:

Arrived by:

Highs F/C____ Lows F/C____

Currency:
Exchange: ____ = ____

HOW DO YOU SAY?

Language:
_____

Hello: Goodbye:

Please: Thank you:

Sights
☆☆☆☆☆
☆☆☆☆☆
☆☆☆☆☆
☆☆☆☆☆
☆☆☆☆☆

Cities
☆☆☆☆☆
☆☆☆☆☆
☆☆☆☆☆
☆☆☆☆☆
☆☆☆☆☆

I'll never forget:
_____
_____
_____
_____
_____
_____

OVERALL RATING: ☆☆☆☆☆

Peru

Draw the flag

ARRIVED   DEPARTED

Travel buddies:

Arrived by:

Highs F/C____ Lows F/C____

Currency:

Exchange: _____ = _____

HOW DO YOU SAY?

Language:

_____

Hello: Goodbye:

Please: Thank you:

Sights
☆☆☆☆☆
☆☆☆☆☆
☆☆☆☆☆
☆☆☆☆☆
☆☆☆☆☆

Cities
☆☆☆☆☆
☆☆☆☆☆
☆☆☆☆☆
☆☆☆☆☆
☆☆☆☆☆

I'll never forget:

_____

_____

_____

_____

_____

OVERALL RATING: ☆☆☆☆☆

Suriname

Draw the flag

ARRIVED | DEPARTED

Travel buddies:

Arrived by:

Highs F/C____ Lows F/C____

Currency:

Exchange: ____ = ____

HOW DO YOU SAY?

Language:
_____

Hello:

Goodbye:

Please:

Thank you:

Sights	Cities
☆☆☆☆☆	☆☆☆☆☆
☆☆☆☆☆	☆☆☆☆☆
☆☆☆☆☆	☆☆☆☆☆
☆☆☆☆☆	☆☆☆☆☆
☆☆☆☆☆	☆☆☆☆☆

I'll never forget:
_____
_____
_____
_____
_____
_____

OVERALL RATING: ☆☆☆☆☆

Uruguay

Draw the flag

ARRIVED | DEPARTED

Travel buddies:

Arrived by:

Highs F/C____ Lows F/C____

Currency:

Exchange: ____ = ____

HOW DO YOU SAY?

Language:

_____

Hello:

Please:

Goodbye:

Thank you:

Sights

☆☆☆☆☆
☆☆☆☆☆
☆☆☆☆☆
☆☆☆☆☆
☆☆☆☆☆

Cities

☆☆☆☆☆
☆☆☆☆☆
☆☆☆☆☆
☆☆☆☆☆
☆☆☆☆☆

I'll never forget:

_____
_____
_____
_____
_____

OVERALL RATING: ☆☆☆☆☆

Venezuela

Draw the flag

ARRIVED   DEPARTED

Travel buddies:

Arrived by:

Highs F/C____   Lows F/C____

Currency:

Exchange: ____ = ____

HOW DO YOU SAY?

Language:
_____

Hello:

Goodbye:

Please:

Thank you:

Sights

☆☆☆☆☆
☆☆☆☆☆
☆☆☆☆☆
☆☆☆☆☆
☆☆☆☆☆

Cities

☆☆☆☆☆
☆☆☆☆☆
☆☆☆☆☆
☆☆☆☆☆
☆☆☆☆☆

I'll never forget:
_____
_____
_____
_____
_____
_____

OVERALL RATING: ☆☆☆☆☆

Draw the flag

_____

Special territory/Other

ARRIVED   DEPARTED

Travel buddies:

Arrived by:

Highs F/C____ Lows F/C____

Currency:

Exchange: _____ = _____

HOW DO YOU SAY?

Language:

_____

Hello: Goodbye:

Please: Thank you:

Sights
☆☆☆☆☆
☆☆☆☆☆
☆☆☆☆☆
☆☆☆☆☆
☆☆☆☆☆

Cities
☆☆☆☆☆
☆☆☆☆☆
☆☆☆☆☆
☆☆☆☆☆
☆☆☆☆☆

I'll never forget:

_____
_____
_____
_____
_____

OVERALL RATING: ☆☆☆☆☆

Special Territories

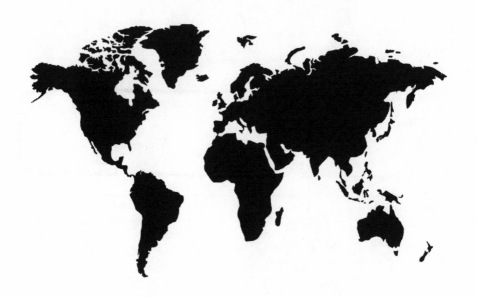

You can't have a narrow mind and a thick passport.

—Pauline Frommer

Draw the flag

_____
Special territory/Other

ARRIVED | DEPARTED

Travel buddies:

Arrived by:
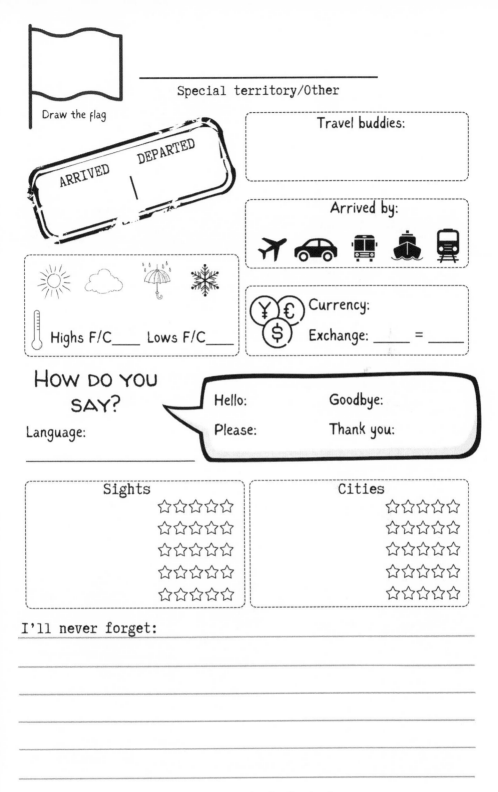

Highs F/C____ Lows F/C____

Currency:
Exchange: ____ = ____

HOW DO YOU SAY?

Language:
_____

Hello:

Goodbye:

Please:

Thank you:

Sights
☆☆☆☆☆
☆☆☆☆☆
☆☆☆☆☆
☆☆☆☆☆
☆☆☆☆☆

Cities
☆☆☆☆☆
☆☆☆☆☆
☆☆☆☆☆
☆☆☆☆☆
☆☆☆☆☆

I'll never forget:

_____
_____
_____
_____
_____

OVERALL RATING: ☆☆☆☆☆☆

Draw the flag

Special territory/Other

ARRIVED | DEPARTED

Travel buddies:

Arrived by:

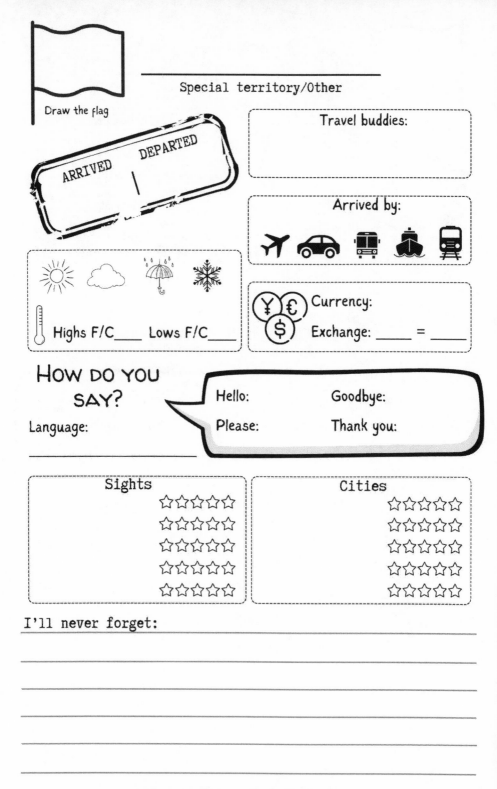

Highs F/C____ Lows F/C____

Currency:

Exchange: ____ = ____

HOW DO YOU SAY?

Language:
_____

Hello:

Goodbye:

Please:

Thank you:

Sights
☆☆☆☆☆
☆☆☆☆☆
☆☆☆☆☆
☆☆☆☆☆
☆☆☆☆☆

Cities
☆☆☆☆☆
☆☆☆☆☆
☆☆☆☆☆
☆☆☆☆☆
☆☆☆☆☆

I'll never forget:
_____
_____
_____
_____
_____

OVERALL RATING: ☆☆☆☆☆

Draw the flag

_____
Special territory/Other

ARRIVED | DEPARTED

Travel buddies:

Arrived by:

Highs F/C____ Lows F/C____

Currency:
Exchange: _____ = _____

HOW DO YOU SAY?

Language:
_____

Hello:

Goodbye:

Please:

Thank you:

Sights
☆☆☆☆☆
☆☆☆☆☆
☆☆☆☆☆
☆☆☆☆☆
☆☆☆☆☆

Cities
☆☆☆☆☆
☆☆☆☆☆
☆☆☆☆☆
☆☆☆☆☆
☆☆☆☆☆

I'll never forget:
_____
_____
_____
_____
_____

OVERALL RATING: ☆☆☆☆☆

Draw the flag

_____
Special territory/Other

ARRIVED   DEPARTED

Travel buddies:

Arrived by:

Highs F/C____ Lows F/C____

Currency:
Exchange: _____ = _____

HOW DO YOU SAY?

Language:
_____

Hello: Goodbye:

Please: Thank you:

Sights	Cities
☆☆☆☆☆	☆☆☆☆☆
☆☆☆☆☆	☆☆☆☆☆
☆☆☆☆☆	☆☆☆☆☆
☆☆☆☆☆	☆☆☆☆☆
☆☆☆☆☆	☆☆☆☆☆

I'll never forget:

_____
_____
_____
_____
_____

OVERALL RATING: ☆☆☆☆☆

Draw the flag

Special territory/Other

ARRIVED | DEPARTED

Travel buddies:

Arrived by:

Highs F/C____ Lows F/C____

Currency:
Exchange: ____ = ____

HOW DO YOU SAY?

Language:
_____

Hello: Goodbye:

Please: Thank you:

Sights
☆☆☆☆☆
☆☆☆☆☆
☆☆☆☆☆
☆☆☆☆☆
☆☆☆☆☆

Cities
☆☆☆☆☆
☆☆☆☆☆
☆☆☆☆☆
☆☆☆☆☆
☆☆☆☆☆

I'll never forget:
_____
_____
_____
_____
_____

OVERALL RATING: ☆☆☆☆☆

Draw the flag

_____

Special territory/Other

Travel buddies:

ARRIVED   DEPARTED

Arrived by:

Highs F/C____ Lows F/C____

Currency:

Exchange: ____ = ____

HOW DO YOU SAY?

Language:

_____

Hello: Goodbye:

Please: Thank you:

Sights
☆☆☆☆☆
☆☆☆☆☆
☆☆☆☆☆
☆☆☆☆☆
☆☆☆☆☆

Cities
☆☆☆☆☆
☆☆☆☆☆
☆☆☆☆☆
☆☆☆☆☆
☆☆☆☆☆

I'll never forget:

_____
_____
_____
_____
_____
_____

OVERALL RATING: ☆☆☆☆☆

Draw the flag

_____
Special territory/Other

ARRIVED   DEPARTED

Travel buddies:

Arrived by:

Currency:
Exchange: _____ = _____

Highs F/C____ Lows F/C____

HOW DO YOU SAY?

Language:
_____

Hello: Goodbye:

Please: Thank you:

Sights
☆☆☆☆☆
☆☆☆☆☆
☆☆☆☆☆
☆☆☆☆☆
☆☆☆☆☆

Cities
☆☆☆☆☆
☆☆☆☆☆
☆☆☆☆☆
☆☆☆☆☆
☆☆☆☆☆

I'll never forget:
_____
_____
_____
_____
_____

OVERALL RATING: ☆☆☆☆☆

Made in the USA
Columbia, SC
15 November 2023

26228913R00136